Assessment and Treatment of Dissociative Identity Disorder

Assessment and Treatment of Dissociative Identity Disorder

Elaine Ducharme Ph.D., ABPP

Published by TPI Press, The Practice Institute, LLC, Camp Hill, PA 17011
All rights reserved. Published 2015
Printed in the United States of America

ISBN: 0990344517
ISBN 13: 9780990344513
Library of Congress Control Number: 2014921757
Published by TPI Press, The Practice Institute, LLC,
Camp Hill, PA

Contents

Dedication

Since my days in graduate school, vast amounts of knowledge have been accumulated about complex trauma and dissociative identity disorder. Yet even today, there are those who doubt the very existence of this disorder. As a young clinician, I was totally unprepared for my first experience with a "multiple," as these patients were called in the 1980s. As discussed in this book, I scrambled to learn whatever I could about this fascinating condition. I am grateful to so many people from whom I learned so much.

But this book would never have been written without the amazing privilege that so many victims of complex trauma have given me by letting me accompany them on their path to healing and integration. I am continuously amazed by the strength of individuals who fight so hard to survive horrific events, even at a very young age. It is my sincere hope that this book will help clinicians understand and appreciate the creativity of this disorder and find the information provided helpful as they work with their own patients.

I must thank Steve Walfish, Jeff Zimmerman, and The Practice Institute for believing in me and this book. Elizabeth Budd's edits have been enormously helpful. A special thanks to Dr. Lenore Walker for her content review and amazingly kind words. She has been an incredible leader in this complicated world of trauma and domestic violence.

I am one of the lucky ones. My parents allowed me to grow up in a home filled with love and respect. They understood boundaries, kept me safe, and then let me fly.

I have also been blessed with wonderful children, Maida, Greta, Jennifer, and Jeffrey, and seven amazing grandchildren. Grandchildren make all the stress of parenting worthwhile.

To my husband, Denny, my strength, my companion, and love of my life. Thank you for holding on and for waiting such a long time for me to say "yes." You, too, know how to keep me safe and also let me fly.

Introduction

Over the years, experienced clinicians have continued to doubt the existence of dissociative identity disorder (DID) and have argued over the best form of treatment for this cluster of symptoms. My goal in writing this book was to provide background information on DID and identify a comprehensive, integrated approach for diagnosis and treatment. I discuss appropriate history taking and identify specific red flags to watch for that may indicate the presence of DID. I review the structure and function of the *alter personality system* and discuss how to work effectively with the many types of alters. Information on how to deal with particularly difficult situations in alters such as suicidal ideation, homicidal thoughts and behaviors, substance abuse, eating disorders, and health problems that are present in only one or a few alters. Specific treatment techniques that foster a safe and effective clinical environment are discussed with an emphasis on maintaining healthy boundaries for both the patient and the psychotherapist. Case history examples are provided throughout to enhance learning. Reasons and techniques for integration are discussed. Finally, a review of the naysayers, those who deny the existence of DID, is presented. Believe me, they exist and at times can make treatment very complicated.

I have worked in the area of trauma and abuse for more than 34 years. I began seeing abused children when I worked as a nurse on a pediatric unit in the 1970s. People didn't really talk about sexual abuse at that time. I frequently heard physicians blame torn hymens in young children on falls from a bicycle. Venereal diseases in young kids were simply "caught" from a toilet seat. And I was told that the mentally retarded 12-year-old African American girl who had just delivered a baby was "fine" and "the pregnancy was part of her culture." Something certainly didn't feel right to me. I began asking a lot of questions and came up with very different answers. One physician commented that since I had started working at the hospital, they were seeing a lot of abused kids. He wondered what I was doing. I responded simply. I told him I was asking questions.

At that point in my career, however, I knew little if anything about DID. As a result, I didn't even know the right questions to ask. As I moved forward in my schooling and received my PhD, I still learned little. It wasn't until I was in private practice and met my first "multiple" that my real education in DID began. I hope to be able to share with you what I have learned. My patients have taught me far more about the human spirit and resilience than I have ever learned from books. They have agreed to let me share their stories. I have agreed to be honest both about my best moments and some of my less-than-stellar moments. It is only through this honest approach that I believe we can all grow.

one

Dissociative Disorders: What Are They?

Imagine suddenly finding yourself in the middle of the supermarket at 10 o'clock at night. You have a basket full of groceries but have no recollection of how you got to the market, how long you have been there, or of putting the groceries in your cart. Your head feels a bit funny and last you remember, you were sitting on the sofa at home with your husband. You check your cell phone and discover several messages from your husband asking where you are. He wonders why it is taking you so long to pick up one prescription at the pharmacy. A total stranger notices you look a bit shaken and asks if you are OK. You don't know what to say

Or perhaps you find your daughter walking out the door one evening. You ask her where she is going, and she reminds you that she is going to her friend's party. You tell her that she does not have permission to do this. She tells you that she discussed the party with you the day before and you clearly gave her permission. You have no recollection of the conversation, and you and your daughter get into an argument that ends with her yelling that she can never trust you to keep your word.

These types of events are common for individuals with dissociative identity disorder (DID). They are also scary, especially before a patient has been properly diagnosed. Often these patients feel crazy or believe that something terrible is going on in their brain.

DID, formerly known as multiple personality disorder (MPD), is defined in the fifth edition of the *Diagnostic and Statistical Manual of Mental Disorders* (*DSM–5*; American Psychiatric Association, 2013) as follows:

A. Disruption of identity that is characterized by two or more distinct personality states, which may be described in some cultures as an experience of possession. The disruption in identity involves marked discontinuity in sense of self and sense of agency, accompanied by related alterations in affect, behavior, consciousness, memory perception, cognition and or sensory functioning

B. Recurrent gaps in the recall of everyday events, important personal information and and/or traumatic events that is consistent with ordinary forgetting.

C. The symptoms cause clinically significant distress or impairment in social, occupational, and other important areas of functioning.

D. The disturbance is not a normal part of a broadly accepted cultural or religious practice (e.g., if in children, the symptoms are better explained by imaginary playmates or fantasy play).

E. The symptoms are not attributable to the direct physiological effects of a substance (e.g., blackouts or chaotic behavior during alcohol intoxication) or another medical condition (e.g., complex partial seizures).

The rationale for these changes for diagnostic criteria from the fourth edition (text revision) of the *DSM* (*DSM–IV–TR*) include a clarification of language noting that different states can be reported or observed. The hope is that this will reduce the use of the diagnosis of DID, not otherwise specified. It was felt that mentioning the "experience of possession" and using criteria for dissociative trance disorder, which was part of *DSM–IV*, increases global utility. The new criteria note that amnesia for everyday events is a common feature.

The *International Classification of Diseases, 10th Revision*, includes a code for DID (F44.81).

DID as a Complex Psychological Trauma

Ford and Courtois (2009) defined complex psychological trauma as resulting from exposure to severe stressors that are (a) repetitive or prolonged, (b) involve harm or abandonment by caregivers or other ostensibly responsible adults, and (c) occur at developmentally vulnerable times in the victim's life, such as early childhood or adolescence. These are critical periods of brain development. Complex posttraumatic sequelae are the changes in mind, emotions, body, and relationships experienced after complex psychological trauma. These include severe problems with dissociation, emotional dysregulation, somatic distress, or relational or spiritual alienation. Clearly, DID can be viewed as fitting into this category because the complex trauma that precedes the development of this disorder constitutes objective threats not only to physical and emotional survival but also to the development and survival of the actual self. These factors must be understood to provide safe and effective treatment.

Historical Perspective

Descriptions of similar disorders go back as far as religious beliefs and behaviors can be traced, and such disorders were often considered to be evidence of "possession states." Pierre Janet, a French scholar born in 1859, was a professor at the Lyceum in Le Havre, France, when he was introduced to a patient, Leonie. Janet began a set of experiments with this patient and others suffering from amnesias, fugues, and "successive existences" (his description of alter personalities) and conversion symptoms. He postulated that these symptoms were attributable to the existence of split-off parts of the personality, which he conceptualized as "subconscious fixed ideas" capable of independent life and development. He demonstrated that the dissociated elements associated with the patients' behaviors had their origin in traumatic experiences and could be treated by bringing into consciousness the split-off memories and affects (Putnam, 1989).

In the United States, Boris Sidis pursued the question of suggestibility in both normal and abnormal subjects. Born at Kieff, Russia, in 1868, he immigrated to the United States when he was 20 years old. He received an MD degree from Harvard and spent a number of years working in Brookline, Massachusetts, engaged in research. Ultimately, he moved to New Hampshire where he worked in the private practice of psychotherapy but also continued his research. Sidis was one of the first to undertake true scientific exploration of the subconscious region of the mind, and his findings were both varied and of practical importance. His formulation of the law of reserve energy and of the principal factors in suggestion, his demonstration of the value of the hypnoidal method as a means of gaining access to the subconscious, and his exposition of the part played by the self-regarding instinct and by overdevelopment of the fear instinct in the causation of psycho-pathic maladies alone suffice to give him a conspicuous place in the history of both psychology and scientific psychotherapy (Bruce, 1923).

Sidis concluded that within every person are two streams of con-sciousness that constitute two separate selves, the waking self and the subwaking self (Crabtree, 1986). Sidis believed that the subwaking self was devoid of morality, willing to carry out any act, susceptible to the emotional forces aroused by crowds and mobs, and without will or goals of its own (Dictionary of American Biography).

Morton Prince, founder of the *Journal of Abnormal Psychology*, was practicing physician who taught neurology at Harvard Medical School from 1895 to 1898 and at Tufts College Medical School, from 1902 to 1912. Among the first to use hypnosis for exploring psychopathology and for psychotherapy, he recognized motivational forces of emotional conflict (Putnam, 1989). He continued Janet's work on dissociation but suggested replacing the term **subconscious** with **coconscious**, which he felt more clearly expressed the coactivity of the second conscious-ness. He deemphasized the importance of amnesia and made the simultaneous activity of two or more systems within one individual the crucial factor in his model of dissociation. He is best known for his work with the MPD patient "Miss Beauchamp" (Crabtree, 1986), which he described in detail in *Dissociation of a Personality* (Prince, 1906).

Others who worked in this area were William James and Frederick Myers. James felt that the "mind seemed to embrace a confederation of psychic entities" (quoted in Taylor, 1982). Myers postulated that there was a second self, which he termed *subliminal self.* The second self was the individual's true or greater self. The conscious self, or *supraliminal self,* was merely a subordinate stream of consciousness required to exer-cise those activities necessary for existence in the world. Myers felt the subliminal self had an existence separate from normal consciousness and actually survived bodily death. The inferior functions of the sublimi-nal self included the amnesias and automatisms associated with psycho-pathology. However, its superior functions included creativity and were manifested in works of genius that involved an uprush of sentiments and feelings from below normal consciousness. He felt that hypnosis and suggestion produced their effects by influencing the subliminal region, and through this region, communication with the spirits of the dead was sometimes possible. Myers felt that phenomena such as multiple personality, spirit possession, and religious ecstasy fell on a continuum that reflected the extent to which the subliminal self intruded in to the waking life (Spanos, 1996). James saw what he described as hysterics as incipient mediums who were subject to pathological dissociations and multiple personalities and who were particularly likely to have their subliminal regions open to spirit influences (Kenny, 1981).

According to Kihlstrom and McConkey (1990), James construed hypnosis as a social interaction in which one person (the hypnotist) offers suggestions to another (the subject) for experiences involving alteration in perception, memory, and voluntary action. In these discussions, he covered all the classic phenomena: ideomotor and challenge suggestions, positive and negative hallucinations, age-regression and other delusions, posthypnotic suggestion, and posthypnotic amnesia. He felt that hypnotic analgesia was powerful enough to use in surgical procedures.

He was quite clear that the phenomena of hypnosis represented disruption of the monitoring and control functions of ordinary waking consciousness. He believed that such a division in consciousness, so dramatically apparent in cases of hysteria and multiple personality, occurred to a lesser degree in hypnosis. James also understood that the major phenomenon of hypnosis could be shaped by expectations and communications arising from the hypnotist, other subjects, and from the general milieu. He correctly discounted purported demonstrations that hypnotic suggestion can coerce antisocial or self-injurious behavior.

Although these men took an experimental approach toward the phenomena of dissociation, most of their work was based on studies of single individuals. Prince's primary experimental interest was in establishing that simultaneous "coconscious" processes were in fact conscious and not merely purely automatic physiological processes. However, he did recognize that one of the coconscious processes might influence the functioning of the other.

In the late 1920s, Messerschmidt (Putnam, 1989) demonstrated the existence of a significant amount of interference between simultaneous conscious and subconscious tasks. He postulated that these symptoms were attributable to the existence of split-off parts of the personality, which he conceptualized as "subconscious fixed ideas" capable of independent life and development. He demonstrated that the dissociated elements associated with the patient's behaviors had their origin in traumatic experiences and could be treated by bringing into consciousness the split-off memories and affects.

During the 1930s, dissociation was no longer considered to be appropriate for legitimate scientific investigation. Psychoanalysts such as Freud and Breuer believed that the cases of MPD that clinicians reported were hypnotic artifacts unwittingly or deliberately induced by the clinician. It is important to know that even today there are psychotherapists who believe this to be the case. Nicholas Spanos (1996), in *Multiple Identities and False Memories: A Sociocognitive Perspective,* his last book written before his death, presents a controversial view of DID. He argues that DID and the recovery of repressed memories of childhood physical and sexual abuse is not a naturally occurring disorder but rather a social construct that exists in a particular cultural and historical framework. This is discussed in further detail in Chapter 12.

The denial of DID by medical and psychiatric personnel can certainly lead to significant problems. For example, a few years ago, I ran into a difficult situation when Ellen, a 38-year-old DID patient I was treating, became paranoid and self-destructive after experiencing a serious retraumatization by a former abuser and was briefly hospitalized. Unfortunately, things went badly in the hospital. On her first day of admission, a first-year medical resident told me that she thought the patient was faking her symptoms. She admitted she had never seen or treated a patient with DID but had on one occasion seen a show on television where the individual (the Hillside Strangler) had made up the diagnosis/behaviors to avoid criminal prosecution. The unit's chief psychiatrist tried to convince the patient that her alters did not exist and that she should simply ignore them. Needless to say, this caused a fair amount of trauma to this patient; she had come to terms with her DID symptoms and, although not thrilled with her diagnosis initially, felt, for the first time, that there was an explanation of her behaviors and experiences that made sense to her. The hospital staff pushed her to the point that she completely shut down and appeared catatonic. The staff decided she must be having some seizure-like activity. However, an electroencephalogram (EEG) and other expensive medical tests proved negative. Ultimately she left the hospital against medical advice. It took months for her to regain an ability to feel reasonably safe in psychotherapy again.

Interest in the dissociative process returned in the 1970s and 1980s. Interest in hypnosis also intensified. The increased public awareness of severe sexual, physical, and emotional abuse of children led to an interest in the effects of trauma on the individual. This proved to be both positive and negative. The positive was clearly the fact that patients suffering from dissociative disorders were being recognized and receiving treatment. The negative evolved from overzealous or poorly trained psychotherapists who began to identify abuse when it didn't exist. This in turn led to the false memory syndrome (FMS). Some people are highly suggestible, and forgotten abuse can emerge as an explanation for their problems if led, especially under hypnosis, to believe this abuse had occurred. Patients with DID are particularly hypnotizable. Thus, it is important never to use hypnosis to go on a "search and find mission" when looking for an explanation of symptoms.

Definitions and Principles of Dissociation

Most experts agree that dissociation can occur in pathological and nonpathological forms. Some liken it to a continuum from minor dissociations such as daydreaming to the major pathological form of DID. Steinberg and Schnall (2000) describe dissociation as a state of fragmented consciousness involving amnesia, a sense of unreality, and feelings of being disconnected from oneself or one's environment. They see it as a standard human response to trauma—a near universal reaction to a life-threatening event. Courtois (2012) describes dissociation as a skill and a defense. She sees dissociation as occurring on a spectrum. In other words, the ability to dissociate serves to protect an individual from events that they are unable to process at the time.

All of us have experienced a form of dissociation at one time or another. When we drive home from work, we often are thinking about what we have been doing during the day or what we may want to do during the evening. Suddenly we realize that we don't remember passing the gas station or some other landmark that we know is on the way home. We don't really remember driving, and yet we arrive safely at our destination. This is occasionally unsettling because we realize that we seemed to have "spaced out" when driving. But then we recognize that, somehow, a part of our brain was concentrating enough to drive safely and clearly and we did have our eyes on the road. Despite a momentary sense of disconnect, we can account for our time, and if someone spoke to us while we were driving, we would respond appropriately. We would know we had been driving and where we were going.

Patients with DID have spent much of their lives having similar kinds of experiences. However, they often may not arrive at the intended destination. They may "wake up" in a strange city or find unfamiliar clothes in their closet. They really don't know where they have been or even with whom they might have spoken. They often feel scared and, until correctly diagnosed, may even feel "crazy." An important key here is that although the ability to dissociate during early traumatic experiences was highly functional and potentially lifesaving, continuation of these coping skills is generally inappropriate and exposes the individual to further danger both physically and emotionally.

West (1967) defined dissociation as a psychophysiological process in which information—incoming, stored, or outgoing—is actively deflected from integration with its usual or expected associations. In essence, dissociation is a state of experience or behavior in which a discernible alteration in a person's thoughts, feelings, and actions are produced so that for a period of time, certain information is not associated or integrated with other information as it normally or logically would be.

Neurobiology of Dissociation

West's definition seems to fit well with what we are beginning to learn about the neurobiology of dissociation. Dissociation involves a failure to integrate systems of encoded and stored experiences and functions (Nijenhuis & Steele, 2002). van der Kolk (1994) hypothesizes that posttraumatic stress disorder (PTSD) occurs in part when the amygdala, which is responsible for fear learning, overfunctions, and the hippocampus, which is thought to record in memory the spatial and temporal dimensions of experience and to play an important role in the categorization and storage of incoming memory, underfunctions. He suggests that trauma hits the brain "like a hurricane." The amygdala cannot handle the force and shuts down. The incoming information is not stored in a meaningful or organized fashion. Rather, the effect is more like traumatic explosions in the central nervous system.

The limbic system (Figure 1), which includes the amygdala, thalamus and hypothalamus, cingulate gyrus, and basal ganglia, is primitive in the way it interprets incoming information. It is the area of the brain that regulates emotion and memory. It directly connects the lower and higher brain functions, and it influences emotions, visceral responses to those emotions, motivation, mood, and sensations of pain and pleasure.

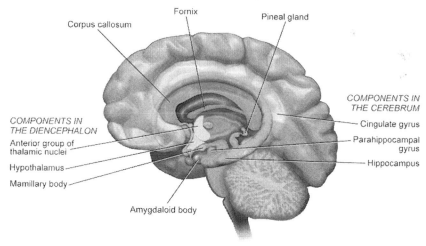

Figure 1. The limbic system. From Blausen.com staff. (2014). Blausen gallery 2014. *Wikiversity Journal of Medicine.* DOI:10.15347/wjm/2014.010. ISSN 20018762. Retrieved from https://en.wikiversity.org/wiki/Blausen_gallery_2014#mediaviewer/File:Blausen_0614_LimbicSystem.png

Language is not a part of the limbic system's repertoire. Rather, the incoming information is interpreted as images and sensations. We make meaning of information in the frontal lobes of the brain where feelings and thoughts join together and construct a story of our experiences. The integrative failure that is characteristic of traumatized individuals may relate to structural and functional brain changes. Psychotherapy and the overall processing of these feelings and images may allow an individual to integrate his or her experiences into a whole life history. Some data suggest temporal lobe abnormalities in dissociation. EEG recordings of dissociative patients usually involved temporal and frontal slow wave activity (Putnam, 1997).

An interesting article by Mary Sykes Wylie (2004) that appeared in *Psychotherapy Networker* discusses the limits of talk therapy with patients who have experienced trauma. She noted that after van der Kolk (1994) wrote his article, "The Body Keeps the Score," which reviewed the existing research on the neurobiological underpinnings of traumatic reactions, Scott Ranch, director of the neuroimaging lab at Massachusetts General Hospital, asked van der Kolk if he would like to take a look inside the brains of some of his trauma patients. The neuroimaging team scanned the brains of eight trauma-patient volunteers under two conditions. The first scan was taken while they remembered neutral events in their lives. The second scan taken was when they were exposed to scripted versions of their traumatic memories.

During the scanning, the images actually showed dissociation taking place in the brains of these PTSD patients. When they remembered a traumatic event, the left frontal cortex shut down, particularly Broca's area, the center of speech. However, areas of the right hemisphere associated with emotion states and autonomic arousal lit up, particularly around the amygdala.

Nijenhuis, van der Hart, and Steele (2002) also noted the possible involvement of neurochemicals in dissociation. From a biological point of view, integrative functions can be hampered by the release of neurochemicals provoked by severe threat. Substances such as glutamate norepinephrine, glucocorticoids, and endogenous opiates, among others, interfere with integration and are dose-dependent. Memory impairment in rats was found to depend on experimental conditions

such as degree of arousal produced by the learning si
strength of the memory involved. Retention of recent
rial was enhanced when moderate doses of epinephr
istered after training, but impaired at high doses. Patients with PTSD
and dissociative disorders, including DID, may alternate between
hyperamnesia and memory loss. Hence, memory retrieval may depend
on the dissociative part of the personality that is dominant.

There is also some evidence that individuals with DID have a
smaller hippocampal volume (Stein, Koverola, Hanna, Torchia, &
McClarty, 1997). A study completed by Vermetten, Schmahl, Lindner,
Loewenstein, and Bremner (2006) demonstrated smaller hippocampal and amygdala volumes in female patients with DID compared
with healthy female subjects. The patients with DID showed a 19.2%
smaller hippocampal volume and a 31.6% smaller amygdala volume.
Clearly, the neurobiology of trauma is a huge area to be explored.
Understanding what is actually happening in the brains of patients
who develop DID will allow us greater understanding of the disorder
and lead to better means of diagnosis and treatment.

Basic Principles of Dissociation

There are three basic principles of dissociation identified by
Nemiah (1981). The first is that the disturbance of identity may take
a variety of forms. For example, the individual can have complete
amnesia about the self, including name and age, which can occur in
psychogenic amnesia or fugue states, or the existence of the alternating identities seen in DID. The second principle is that there will be
a disturbance in the individual's memory for events occurring during the period of dissociation. The third principle is that the vast
majority of dissociative disorders are traumatically induced. Christine
Courtois (2012), in a presentation for the Psychotherapy Networker
Conference, noted that dissociation has also been linked to studies
of attachment and family dynamics. It appears logical that in families
in which severe abuse was occurring, there would also be difficulties
with attachment. Parents who truly love and feel attached to their off-
spring would be far less likely to inflict the intensity of harm necessary
for DID to develop. It is generally accepted that for DID to emerge,

severe recurrent trauma would typically have to have occurred during early childhood, generally before age 11. Waseem, Aslam, Switzer, and Perales (2007) identify the origin of DID as occurring between 2.5 and 8 years with issues around this arising in early adolescence.

Although men and women who have experienced horrific trauma during wartime may experience dissociative episodes, they do not de facto develop DID. Rather, they may experience psychogenic amnesia or fugue reactions. Because the trauma has occurred after they have reached young adulthood, their sense of individual self was established well before the occurrence of the traumatic incident.

two

Critical Review of Dissociative Identity

Disorder as a Diagnosis

As I noted in Chapter 1, there are still those who deny the existence of dissociative identity disorder (DID). Most critics of DID seem to agree that the behavior named by this diagnosis is socially learned. Nicholas Spanos (1996) was particularly vocal about this issue. Dr. Spanos was Professor of Psychology and Director of the Laboratory of Experimental Hypnosis at Carlton University. His last book, *Multiple Identities and False Memories,* and published after his death and provides what he describes as a "sociocognitive" perspective on the subject of multiple identities. He conducted many experiments in his own laboratory, which he later used to draw his conclusions. Spanos argued that the idea that multiple personality disorder (MPD; now termed DID) is a naturally occurring mental disorder is fundamentally flawed. He proposed that multiple identities can be understood as rule-governed social constructions established, legitimized, and maintained through social instruction. He believed that neither a history of abuse nor severe psychopathology was necessary for the maintenance of multiple identities.

Spanos saw hypnotic behavior, including hypnotic amnesia, to be a strategic behavior enacted to fulfill the subject's beliefs and expectations about hypnosis. He went on to point out that theories of MPD (DID) based on the premise that hypnotic behaviors occur during some altered state or that hypnotic and nonhypnotic behaviors are processed or stored in different ways, are completely invalid.

Spanos (1996) felt that one of the more alarming claims about MPD (DID) was that some patients had been subjected to ritualistic abuse at the hands of Satanists or other cult groups. He felt it was often asserted that these patients had been exposed to powerful brainwashing techniques that had transformed them into "robotic automata." He felt strongly that not only is brainwashing not effective and therefore could not provide an explanation for the development of MPD but that the very existence of satanic groups could not be established

Spanos (1996) and others believe that the regular co-occurrence of sexual abuse memories and DID resulted from the confluence of several sociohistorical trends. The first involved a reawakening of interest in DID during a period of intense societal interest in the topic of child abuse. In the 1970s, largely as a result of the feminist movement, public attention focused on sexual aggression against women and on the complicity of existing social institutions in fostering, or at least tolerating, such aggression. These two issues came together to produce a growing concern about the sexual abuse of children and the prevalence and consequences of such abuse.

Merskey (1992) reviewed a large number of cases from the 20th century and earlier that provided information about treatment procedures and symptomatology of DID. He believed that the rise in DID diagnosis can be traced to the influence of books and films including *The Three Faces of Eve* (Thigpen & Cleckly, 1957) and *Sybil* (Schreiber, 1973). Merskey (1992) went on to report that he had found highly leading and suggestive procedures used in the diagnosis of MPD (DID). He has referred to DID as the "manufacture of madness." The character of Sybil (Schreiber, 1973) was reported to have suffered horrendous physical and sexual abuse during early childhood. Spanos (1996) felt that *Sybil* encouraged therapists to look for and find evidence of severe child abuse in cases of DID. Spanos (1996) also pointed out that a number of highly experienced clinicians report never having seen a case of MPD.

McHugh (1992) argued that hysteria, what he saw as the DID patient's

more or less unconscious effort to appear more significant to others and to be more entitled to their interest and support, along with the current social canonization of the victim, accounts for the fanciful behavior of those who claim to have multiple identities and personalities. (p. 500)

He called the diagnosis a *psychiatric misadventure.*

More recently, Traub (2009) focused on whether DID could be reliably identified and validly categorized. In assessing four factors—childhood trauma, prevalence ratings, media influences, and psychophysiological perspectives—he ultimately concluded that evidence either supporting or opposing the validity of current categorization of this disorder seems unconvincing and inconclusive. He pointed out that it is difficult to assess the intensity, duration, and kind of abuse that lead to this disorder. He noted that the prevalence ratings highlight the dramatic increase of the diagnosis in the 1980s, with perspectives supporting both the underdiagnosis and overdiagnosis of DID. He then pointed out that with the growth of popular books about patients with DID, such as *Sybil, Michelle Remembers,* and *The Three Faces of Eve,* there was an increase not only in the number of reported cases but also in the number of alternate personalities a patient might have, which increased from a typical two or three to approximately 15 alters. He suggested the possibility that the expectations of the mental health professional may have unwittingly encouraged the development of additional alters, thereby diminishing the validity of DID as a diagnosis. Finally, he noted that although some EEG studies showed differences in the brain activity of each personality, other studies did not support these results. In contrast, Birnbaum and Thompson (1996) reported a difference in visual capacities between alters, and a twin study conducted by Jang, Paris, Zweig-Frank, and Liversly (1998) demonstrated that genetic influences played a role in DID development. Nonetheless, Traub (2009) felt that psychophysiological perspectives on DID remain shrouded in doubt.

Shaffer and Oakley (2005) argued that DID is best interpreted as a causal model of a possible posttraumatic process, a mechanical model of an abnormal psychological condition. They stated that there is no good reason to demonstrate that anyone has ever suffered from DID because the proponents of DID violate the basic methodological principles of good causal modeling. In their discussion of memory, they described their belief that many of the "memories" that are brought up regarding DID patients' pasts are plausibly the result of iatrogenic suggestion and that the practice of recovering repressed memories is fundamentally misguided and based on a highly dubious account of how memory works.

Piper and Mersky (2004), in an article titled "The Persistence of Folly: Critical Examination of Dissociative Identity Disorder," argued that the concept of DID is illogical. They stated that the diagnostic and treatment methods of DID proponents encourage patients to behave as if they have multiple selves. They also suggested that the vague and elastic definition of *alter personality* makes a reliable diagnosis of DID impossible. They pointed out that most patients show no signs of multiplicity before being diagnosed with DID.

Every patient whom I ultimately diagnosed with DID reported symptoms of loss of time, described being told of behaviors or actions they had done but did not recall, or presented an alter, very different from the initial patient presentation to me, well before the diagnosis. I believe that many patients do not realize they are presenting to different people in different ways. If told something they do not recall, they chalk it up to forgetfulness or sometimes worry that they are "crazy." Furthermore, the most florid symptoms of DID often do not appear until individuals reach their 20s or 30s, often after many false diagnoses (Kluft, 1985). It is also important to be aware that many who argue against the existence of DID insist these patients are really suffering from severe borderline personality disorder. Yet even borderline patients who are labile do not have emotions and behaviors that indicate the presence of actual alters.

Conclusions

I would agree that it is difficult, if not impossible, to remove all cultural influence from the diagnosis of DID and many other mental illnesses. However, it is equally as important to understand why a patient's life is being lived as it is. In other words, what do specific symptoms mean? I was not looking for the diagnosis and was rather skeptical of its existence when I first discovered behaviors consistent with DID in a patient. I had not tried to hypnotize the woman or tried to elicit the appearance of any alters. A highly functioning nurse, whom I had been seeing in psychotherapy for several months, arrived at my office complaining of a headache. She lay down on the couch and shut her eyes. I thought she had fallen asleep, but then her eyes opened and a young child who didn't seem to know me appeared to be present in both voice and mannerisms.

Only one of my patients ever seemed truly comfortable with the initial diagnosis, and with this individual, I remained skeptical. The rest of my DID patients found the diagnosis disturbing on the one hand but, on the other hand, comforting as an explanation for many of the difficulties they had been dealing with throughout their lives. They reported that they had always just assumed they must be crazy because of the "black holes" in time and the voices in their heads. At some level, the diagnosis came as a relief. Traditional psychoanalytic theory stresses the need for symptoms to be understood. It is in this frame of reference that I believe DID, as well as many other illnesses, must be treated. If dissociation has helped a person survive a history of severe trauma, the psychotherapist must respect these behaviors and work with them. I have experienced the challenges and rewards of helping individuals learn to accept their past history and develop new, nondissociative coping skills. I am generally skeptical of an individual psychotherapist who claims to have a lot of DID patients in his or her practice at any given time, in part because it is not that common and in part because it would be too taxing on any one clinician. Nonetheless, I remain firm in my belief that DID does indeed exist and is an example of the extraordinary coping mechanisms that human beings use for survival.

three

Types of Dissociative Reactions

There are a number of types of dissociative responses and altered states. One National Institute of Mental Health survey, reported by Putnam, Guroff, Silberman, Barban, and Post (1986), noted the most common dissociative symptoms in DID patients to be as follows: amnesias (98%), fugue episodes (55%), feelings of depersonalization (53%), and sleepwalking (20%). Bliss (1984) described essentially the same profile, led by amnesias (85%), dazed states (83%), depersonalization (54%), and fugue states (52%).

Hypnoid or *trancelike* states appear to be an ego defense to trauma and have been identified as a powerful predictor of early DID in children and adolescents (Putnam, 1989). *Somnambulism,* or sleepwalking, is common in childhood and generally disappears by around age 10. However, sleepwalking that continues into adulthood often has a later childhood age of onset and is more frequently accompanied by the presence of psychopathology. A major life event is frequently associated with the onset of sleepwalking in adult somnambulism and is less often found in the histories of individuals who outgrew their sleepwalking.

Somnambulism in adults may be part of the clinical picture of DID. In patients with DID, it is often caused by the emergence of alters, often children, either acting out forbidden impulses, abreacting trauma, or simply playing. I have several patients who have reported unexplained messes in the house or family members finding them cleaning, drawing or writing, bathing, showering, or engaged in other behaviors of which they have no memory in the morning. One woman's husband occasionally found her trying to make sandwiches or cookies and seeming confused as to how to proceed once the ingredients were on the counter. Upon investigation, it turned out that a young alter was out and trying to cook.

Psychogenic amnesia, also referred to as *dissociative amnesia,* is an inability to recall important personal information, usually of a traumatic or stressful nature, that is too extensive to be explained by ordinary forgetfulness and is not associated with an organic mental disorder (American Psychiatric Association, 2000). Most often the missing personal information involves the individual's identity and may include name, age, marital status, occupational information, and personal life history (Rapaport, 1971). People with psychogenic amnesia are usually aware that they are unable to recall important personal information, although they may exhibit *la belle indifférence* toward their impairment. For example, they may not appear to be particularly upset that they are suffering what appears to be a paralysis or some other physical symptom. The classic psychoanalytical interpretation of *la belle indifférence* is that it is evidence that an intrapsychic conflict has been converted and kept from its unacceptable conscious expression by the production of a physical symptom—so-called primary gain.

Alexia was 15 when she was sexually abused by a relative while on a trip. She contacted her parents, and they arranged for her to return home immediately. The extended family had always been close. However, when her parents told the extended family, they did not believe her story and supported the older relative. The loss of the affection of so many people was devastating for her. She ran into a grandparent several months after the incident, who acted as if she didn't exist. The next day, the police found Alexia lying in the snow dressed only in her pajamas. She could not recall her name and did not recognize her house, her family, or her friends. During the course of 1 week, she regained little information. Needless to say, I was concerned about what had actually happened and how long these symptoms might last. I spoke with her psychiatrist, who was also unsure how to proceed. I suggested that I could try to use hypnosis in an open and indirect fashion. I would begin with what she was able to recall and use the phases, "What happened just before that?" and "What happened next?" During several hypnosis sessions, she was able to recall the events leading up to the amnesia. A friend, who had been with her when she saw the grandparent, verified these events. It took several weeks for her to gain total recall of the more intimate details of her life, but she did fully recover. It is now many years later, and she has excelled in college and has a great job. There have been no other episodes of amnesia, and she has reestablished some contact with her relatives.

Dissociative fugue is characterized by sudden, unexpected travel away from one's home or customary place of work, accompanied by an inability to recall one's past and confusion about personal identity or the assumption of a new identity (American Psychiatric Association, 2000). There is often the assumption of a new identity. The travel of someone in a fugue state may seem to be rather aimless. However, it may also include the use of public transportation. They may appear quite normal to the average observer. In contrast to individuals experiencing psychogenic amnesia, people in a fugue state are usually unaware of their loss of self-referential information (Rapaport, 1971).

Many patients with DID dissociate during psychotherapy sessions. Although we discuss the need to assess the "return to previous state" before the patient leaves the office, it is not infrequent that patients who appear to be okay report that they have no real memory of how they got home or what they had done between the office and home. Some report "waking up" in the middle of a store finding numerous articles they didn't need in their shopping cart. They often have spoken with shopkeepers or others in the store. They are unable to identify a particular alter who was out during this time. These incidents appear to be brief fugue states.

Depersonalization disorder is characterized by a persistent or recurring feeling of being detached from one's mental processes or body that is accompanied by intact reality testing (American Psychiatric Association, 2000). The person may report feeling unreal, as if he or she were in a dream, like a machine, dead, self-estranged, or otherwise changed from his or her normal state. Depersonalization is only considered a diagnosable disorder when it occurs in the absence of another disorder, such as DID that includes feelings of depersonalization (Putnam, 1989). Some patients with severe anxiety report having these experiences.

Dissociative disorder, not otherwise specified (NOS), was included in the fourth edition (text revision) of the *Diagnostic and Statistical Manual of Mental Disorders* (*DSM*) for diagnosing disorders in which the prominent feature is a dissociative symptom but that do not meet the criteria for a specific dissociative disorder. The new diagnostic criteria in *DSM–5* were written with the hope of minimizing the use of this category. For example, Cindy, a 62-year-old professional woman, had a long history of physical, emotional, and sexual abuse and was, at the time of her first session, in an abusive marriage. She spoke of her little girl that would come out when she became upset. This "child" would cry inconsolably that she just wanted someone to love her. However, she always was aware of what had happened. She could not always control when this "child" would be out, she knew it was generally after a big fight or traumatic event with her husband or someone relatively close to her. This was never a problem at work. She reported no missing time and no other events typically associated with DID. This alter appeared in one or two sessions for differing periods of time. However, again, she could always tell me what had happened and what she was feeling. In this case, the most appropriate diagnosis for her was dissociative disorder, NOS.

Possession states are another form of dissociation. The *DSM–5*, as noted earlier, includes "an experience of possession" as part of the diagnostic criteria for DID. Primitive cultures and some religious groups have strong beliefs in possession states. The classic psychiatric review of possession states was done by Oesterreich (1966), who felt there were two main forms of possession: a "somnambulistic" or hysterical form, and a lucid or obsessional form. In the lucid form, individuals are aware of themselves but feel invaded and engaged in a struggle for control over their behavior. In the somnambulistic form, individuals have lost all consciousness of the self and speak with the voice of the "intruder." For more extensive review of the history of possession and treatment by exorcism, the reader is directed to Oesterreich (1966) and Pattison and Wintrob (1981). Ellen, the 38-year-old patient with DID mentioned earlier, was able to accept most of her alters after she was diagnosed with DID. However, she truly believed that the persecutor alter was evidence of possession. Many patients, particularly those who have been raised in a religious environment that embraces the concept of possession, have a difficult time accepting that a persecutor alter could actually be a part of themselves.

Near-death and out-of-body experiences may also be seen as forms of dissociation. Putnam (1989) described out-of-body experiences as a time when the individual perceives his or her awareness or mind as being outside or separated from the physical body. This is relatively common in patients with DID. Out-of-body experiences are also relatively common in near-death experiences in individuals who suffer life-threatening trauma or are revived after respiration or heartbeat have ceased. Some people have reported out-of-body experiences during meditation and extreme relaxation.

Finally, a few other unusual psychiatric syndromes are considered forms of dissociation. *Folie à deux* or *folie à plusieurs* have a core feature of the transfer of mental symptoms, particularly paranoid delusions, from one person to another. This syndrome is most commonly diagnosed when the two or more individuals concerned live in proximity and may be socially or physically isolated and have little interaction with other people. For example, a person with a psychotic disorder believes aliens are spying on him or her. The person with shared psychotic disorder will also begin to believe in spying aliens. The delusions are induced in the secondary case and usually disappear when the people are separated. Aside from the delusions, the thoughts and behavior of the secondary case are usually fairly normal. The disorder was first conceptualized in 19th-century French psychiatry by Charles Lasègue and Jean-Pierre Falret and so is also known as *Lasègue-Falret syndrome* (Berrios, in Ireland, 1998). *Le délire de négation* or *Cotard syndrome* involves, in its extreme form, a complete denial of the existence of self. In milder forms, this may be seen as a sense of depersonalization-like change in the self or a feeling of despair or self-loathing (Enoch & Trethowan, 1979).

four

Factors That Influence the Form of

Dissociation

Dissociation is an amazing phenomenon that can be influenced by a variety of factors. This chapter considers various factors—including age, gender, legal issues, ethnic and socioeconomic status, attachment issues, and culture—that influence how a patient's dissociation may manifest. They are discussed in turn.

Age

Dissociative reactions seem to have their origin as an adaptive response to overwhelming trauma. Age at the time of trauma appears to be a significant factor. Dissociative identity disorder (DID) generally develops only when sustained and severe trauma occurs before age 11 or 12. In these cases, there are often multiple perpetrators. After that age, if severe trauma occurs, whether inflicted by another person or persons or resulting from exposure to severe traumatic events the individual has enough ego strength to avoid the more serious development of alters. Although dissociation related to a particular traumatic event or series of events (such as war trauma or witnessing a murder) may occur and certainly posttraumatic stress disorder is common, we do not see sudden-onset DID in adults. However, as noted earlier, the most florid symptoms of DID become more noticeable in adulthood, when the disorder is actually diagnosed. In this case, the DID was present from early childhood, but the symptoms became more pronounced later in life.

There is a remarkable degree of agreement among various experts as to the average age of the DID patient at time of diagnosis. Putnam and Post (1988) reviewed the literature and found a mean age of 28.5 years. Kluft's (1985) research indicates that the clinical presentation of DID varies with age but that the most floridly multiple clinical presentations typically occur within the third and fourth decades, often many years after the onset of symptoms.

Gender

The role of gender in the development of DID has been a bit more difficult to assess. Initially, far more women were reported to have DID. Ratios ranged from 2:1 to as high as 8:1 (Allison, 1974; Putnam, Guroff, Silberman, Barban, & Post 1986). The *Diagnostic and Statistical Manual of Mental Disorders* (*DSM–5*; American Psychiatric Association, 2013) notes the 12-month prevalence of DID among adults in a small U.S. community was 1.5%. The prevalence across genders in that study was 1.6 % for males and 1.4% for females.

Women with DID, like women in general, have a higher tendency to direct their anger at themselves through suicidal behaviors or self-mutilation and therefore may be more likely to come into contact with the mental health system. Men, in general, whether they have received a diagnosis of DID or not, tend to direct feelings of anger outward and therefore get caught in the criminal justice system. This is definitely the case with men having DID. A study by Bliss and Larson (1985) found a relatively high incidence of DID among rapists and sex offenders.

Legal Issues

When working with a criminal population, one must be cautious to assess for malingering. DID can be a handy defense when one is being accused of a crime. On the other hand, it is not uncommon for patients with DID to have alters that do act out, sometimes illegally. Sometimes these are relatively minor issues, such as a child alter stealing a candy bar in a store. Other times a teen may steal drugs. I have had the opportunity to explain the diagnosis to a prosecutor and judge when one of my patients had a teen alter that had been given cocaine by a relative, who then sexually abused her. She ultimately developed a drug problem and stole medication from someone's home. The patient, in her mid-30s, had never been in any trouble with the law before and was horrified when the police issued a warrant for her arrest. She had a teenage son and was a loving mother. She had no recall of the events. However, with some exploring, the teen alter admitted to stealing the drugs. Although I know the prosecutor was a bit skeptical, the judge allowed my patient to enter an alternative treatment program, remain in psychotherapy with me, stay on probation, and avoid jail. The patient and I worked hard in helping the teen alter recognize the trouble she caused the entire system by her actions. She had to confront her problem with drugs and find other ways to use her positive adolescent energy to help the host, deal with emotional pain and abusive family members that continued to be in her life. It is worth noting that the host is generally considered the primary individual who presents for treatment and may not be the birth individual.

There is no absolute way to differentiate true psychogenic amnesia from malingering. Kluft (1988) pointed out that malingerers have been noted to continue their deception even during hypnotically or barbiturate-facilitated interviews. Because of this, it is essential that the clinician be careful not to confuse the role of forensic examiner with that of treating therapist in assessment of an accused individual.

Amnesia due to childhood abuse has been recognized over the years as a legitimate factor in plaintiffs' failure to bring a timely tort action against their abusers within the usual statute of limitations. Many state and federal courts have ruled that the statute of limitations for bringing suit against an abuser begins when the amnesic adult plaintiff becomes aware of the childhood abuse, not when the abuse first occurred. The statute of limitations for criminal action and civil action are generally different and vary by state. Interestingly, when patients are most vulnerable and in the throes of dealing with the trauma, they are least able to cope with the trauma and complexities of a lawsuit. Then, after treatment, when they have regained a sense of self and peace, they often just want to let it go. One of my patients whom I ultimately diagnosed with DID had contacted an attorney about filing a lawsuit against her perpetrators before she began treatment with me. He had refused to take the case because her descriptions of the abuse were completely confusing. Different alters had written the account of what had happened. After treatment and integration, she chose to just move forward with her life. She did not want to bring back old ghosts. This is not always the case. Some victims want to see justice done. This can be very frustrating when the time to press legal charges or file a civil lawsuit has expired.

Ethnic and Socioeconomic Status

The data on ethnic and socioeconomic status are scanty but from what is available, it is evident that DID occurs across all major racial groups and socioeconomic settings (Putnam et al., 1989). My own experience has been that many patients with DID have been raised in extreme fundamentalist religious backgrounds. Women and children tend to be more likely to be abused in these rather rigid cultures. However, whether this is universal needs further documentation.

Lloyd deMause (2002) in a discussion of abuse, noted that in general and in all societies, children and women are particularly vulnerable to abuse. He went on to say "the world is now in a race between our slowly improving child rearing and our rapidly evolving destructive technology" (p. 123). Clearly human rights across the world remain an issue. Sar, Middleton, and Dorahy (2013) noted that, according to the U.S. Department of State, between 10,000 and 15,000 women and girls are trafficked domestically for commercial exploitation. He also noted that Thailand's Health System Research Institute has reported that 40% of Thailand's prostitutes are children. One can only imagine the kinds of experiences these children have and the ways they devise to cope. The March–April 2012 edition of the *Journal Trauma and Dissociation* was devoted to exploring individual and societal oppression and reviewing global perspectives on dissociative disorders. The articles incorporate a conclusion that the substance of cultural differences displayed in syndromes of dissociative individuals has been overplayed. They demonstrate, through a variety of examples, that oppression is part of the human condition in both democratic and undemocratic societies. Where oppression resides, dissociation is, by necessity, a constant companion. It would be interesting to research the actual prevalence of dissociative disorders in this population.

Attachment Issues

Courtois (2012) pointed out that emotional abuse, including neglect and failure to respond and soothe a child, is also implicated in the development of dissociative disorders. This understanding allows us to make a shift back toward the interpersonal patterns started early in life and away from solely working with the trauma. Allen (2013) recalled that when he was speaking to patients in a trauma group, he told them that the mind can be a very scary place. A group member responded, "Yes, and you wouldn't want to go in there alone." Unfortunately, many victims of trauma and patients with DID spend much of their formative years alone, trying to manage events for which they do not even have words. They are hurt and threatened by those who are supposed to provide comfort and protection. No wonder many of them develop alters for comfort and support!

Allen went on to discuss the importance of *mentalizing* in therapy. He described mentalizing as "holding mind in mind." It is maintaining an attitude of inquisitiveness, curiosity, and open-mindedness toward mental states in self and others. Although the concept of mentalizing evolved in relation to psychoanalytic psychotherapy, I agree with Allen that it is "hard to conceive of any approach to therapy, and especially trauma therapy, including prolonged exposure, that does not require mentalizing on the part of the client and therapist" (Allen, 2013, p. 369).

Culture

According to the *DSM–5* (American Psychiatric Association, 2013) many features of DID can be influenced by the individual's cultural background. Individuals with this disorder may present with prominent medically unexplained neurologic symptoms, such as nonepileptic seizures, paralyses, or sensory loss, in cultural settings where such symptoms are common, such as Haiti and other islands where voodoo is practiced. Similarly, in settings where normative possession is common (e.g., rural areas in the developing world, among certain religious groups in the United States and Europe), the fragmented identities may take the form of possessing spirits, deities, demons, animals, or mythical figures. Acculturation or prolonged intercultural contact may shape the characteristics of the other identities (e.g., identities in India may speak English exclusively and wear Western clothes). Possession-form identities in DID typically manifest as behaviors that appear as if a "spirit," supernatural being, or outside person has taken control, such that the individual begins speaking or acting in a distinctly different manner. For example, an individual's behavior may give the appearance that her identity has been replaced by the ghost of a girl who committed suicide in the same community years before, speaking and acting as though she were still alive. Possession-form DID can be distinguished from culturally accepted possession states in that the former is involuntary, distressing, uncontrollable, and often recurrent or persistent. It involves conflict between the individual and his or her surrounding family, social or work milieu. It is manifested at times and places that violate the norms of the culture or religion.

five

Symptom Profile

Multiple Previous Diagnoses

Most patients who are diagnosed with dissociative identity disorder (DID) have had a long history of psychiatric or neurologic symptoms. Many have an average of 10 diagnoses by different clinicians before the correct diagnosis is made. Patients in a 1986 National Institute of Mental Health (NIMH) study, discussed by Putnam (1989), averaged 6.8 years from initial presentation in the mental health system to correct diagnosis. Typical diagnoses include borderline personality disorder (BPD), schizophrenia, depression, schizoaffective disorder, conversion disorders, and temporal lobe epilepsy. Patients may show coexisting signs of obsessive-compulsive disorder, eating disorders, substance abuse problems, and impulse control problems. BPD is a common misdiagnosis because of the switching behaviors among ego states. I have had a number of discussions with colleagues, and in particular several psychiatrists, who consider DID a severe form of BPD.

Depression is the single most common presenting symptom of a patient with DID. However, vegetative symptoms, such as fatigue, lack of interest in daily activities, decreased libido, for example, can be short-lived or even absent in patients with DID. About three-quarters of these patients describe mood swings. Family members may have told them they have frequent mood swings, sometimes several times a day or even multiple times an hour. Patients may have been told that at times they act like a different person.

Bipolar disorder is another common diagnosis made before the correct diagnosis of DID is determined. Clearly it is essential to take a careful and extensive history with these patients to examine for possible underlying process dynamics of a dissociative process.

Multiple Symptoms

More than 70% of outpatients with DID have a history of suicide attempts (American Psychiatric Association, 2013). Suicide gestures as well as self-destructive ideation and behaviors, such as cutting and eating disorders, are also common. It is important to ask about where the cutting is taking place. Many victims of severe sexual abuse will report self-mutilation of genitals and breasts. They often have low self-esteem and are anhedonic. Difficulty concentrating is often reported, as are feelings of fatigue, sexual difficulties, and crying spells.

Rarely do patients enter treatment volunteering information about dissociation. It may take many months of contact for patients to talk about these systems. Because of the lost time, unexplained voices in their heads, confusion about where they have been or what they have done, they often think they are "crazy." The presence of substance abuse can certainly confound the picture and make treatment more complicated. Alcohol, stimulants, and anxiolytics are commonly abused by patients with DID. Drug abuse often begins with the prescription of narcotics for treatment of severe headaches, which are also commonly seen in DID and are often present when "switching" between alters. Though, it may have begun in childhood or early adolescence as a means of coping with the abuse. The drugs or alcohol may also have been given to the person by their offender as part of the abusive behavior.

Patients rarely seem to abuse hallucinogens. They are struggling to stay in contact with reality and avoid any additional "weird experiences." They often feel they are already hallucinating.

Substance Abuse

Psychotherapists may refuse to treat patients who are actively abusing substances. However, sometimes it is important to provide some treatment before the patient is sober. One of my patients with DID so hated herself that the idea she was even worthy enough to stop drinking was impossible for her to accept. We worked for about a year trying to get to a place where she was willing to accept that it was okay for her to accept treatment, and we enlisted the aid of two alters to help in this process. She was then able to enter and successfully complete an inpatient substance abuse program for women. Treatment for the DID issues resumed after she had attained sobriety and was well connected with support.

Hallucinations

As noted earlier, patients with DID report what seem to be hallucinations. Kluft (1987) pointed out that many patients with DID may satisfy many of Schneider's first-order symptoms for a diagnosis of schizophrenia. They hear voices in their heads that berate them or command them to hurt themselves or others. They may hear screaming, laughing, or the crying voice of a child or children in distress. They may also hear some voices that offer consolation, comfort, or advice. Unlike people with schizophrenia, however, who report voices commanding them from outside themselves, these patients generally describe the voices as coming from inside their heads, often as "loud thoughts." They may hear lengthy and coherent conversations unlike the more primary process voices heard by individuals with schizophrenia. Because these experiences occur long before the diagnosis of DID is made, they can be terrifying for patients.

Olfactory and Tactile Hallucinations

Approximately 5% to 12% of patients with DID report the presence of olfactory and tactile hallucinations (Putnam, 1989); however, olfactory hallucinations are more common in patients with temporal lobe abnormalities as documented on electroencephalogram. It is crucial that patients who report olfactory hallucinations be referred for medical evaluation to rule out organic causes. Tactile hallucinations are often experienced as crawling sensations on or under the skin. Patients may be certain that they have some serious and contagious skin condition and spend a lot of time and money visiting dermatologists and scrubbing their bodies, linens, and clothes. Somatic memories, especially pain in the vaginal area and pressure on the chest, as well as feelings of being unable to breathe and frequent gagging, which are common among individuals forced to perform oral sex, can be confused with tactile memories.

Body Distortions

Many patients report seeing changes in their body image. When an alter is out, that is who they see in the mirror. As a result, they may develop an aversion to mirrors. They also describe "autoscopic" hallucinations, seeing themselves from up above or as if watching a movie of themselves. These out-of-body experiences are usually accompanied by profound depersonalization, similar to the reports of near-death experiences. During psychotherapy sessions patients may report disembodied faces floating in the air or bloody or hideous scenes. When this occurs, it is typically associated with the emergence of issues related to past trauma.

Revolving-Door Crisis

At times, especially during early parts of treatment, alters switch so rapidly that a "revolving-door crisis" occurs. Basically, this is a series of alters whizzing in and out in an attempt to gain control. The resulting speech that the clinician hears is often described as a "word salad." It may look to the clinician and feel to the patient like a thought disorder and can be disconcerting, but it is usually transient and can be related to a specific crisis.

Delusions

Delusions can also occur. Often what appears to be a delusion turns out to have a basis in fact when the psychotherapist begins to understand the dynamics of the patient's dissociative pathology. A common example is that many alters believe they can physically harm another personality, a fixed belief that they can separate and hurt another part, without harming themselves. Obviously, this is not true, but until the patient really understands that each alter is really a part of the whole, this belief can have deadly consequences. This is one of those issues, specific to patients with DID, in which contracts about suicide, if used at all, must be carefully constructed. I discuss in

Chapter 6 why suicide and no harm contracts can be dangerous and are generally not recommended. Be aware that alters are clever and will often look for loopholes. Although some patients with DID may have ideas that qualify as truly delusional, one rarely finds that these delusions are of the type generally seen in paranoid disorders in which the patient believes that some external agency, such as the FBI or aliens, are sending them messages through the media or in some other way (Putnam, 1989). The delusions of DID are often those of passive influence experiences that have a basis in fact or delusions of separateness secondary to the excessive narcissistic investments of some alters in their individuality.

Self-Mutilation

About one-third of DID patients report self-mutilation, though this number is probably much higher (Putnam, Guroff, Silberman, Barban, & Post, 1986). They may engage in more typical types of burning or cutting. However, many develop more bizarre habits, which include insertion of foreign objects such as broken glass into the vagina or anus. Many of my patients have reported cutting themselves on their breasts and in the vaginal area.

Catatonia

The NIMH study mentioned earlier (Putnam, 1989) reported that approximately 14% of patients with DID have experiences of catatonia. This may occur when the individual is overwhelmed by outside stimuli that trigger a massive recall of traumatic experiences. It may also be used as a healing experience that filters out, or slows down, the overwhelming stimuli to a tolerable level. Ellen, the 38-year-old DID patient I described earlier, used catatonia to finally feel safe in a hospitalization that had clearly gone badly. For her, it was an adaptive way to escape the retraumatization that was occurring in the hospital.

Headaches

As noted earlier, headaches in patients with DID are common. They are the single most common neurological symptom reported in DID (Putnam, 1989). They can be excruciatingly painful and associated with visual disturbances. They often represent conflicts and struggles for control of the body, forced switching, or punishment by an alter. They often do not respond to typical pain medications. When this occurs during a session, the patient may need to lie down or sit quietly with eyes shut for a few minutes. The headaches generally go away once the "switch" is over. Casey, a 40-year-old woman and my first patient with DID, regularly had severe headaches at the beginning of treatment. However, as treatment progressed, she would sometimes still wince or say "ouch" as a minor pain in her head occurred during a switch or an attempt by another part to take over the conversation.

Additional Sensory Disturbances
Numbness and Tingling Sensations

Patients often report feeling numb in specific body parts or throughout their bodies. These sensations allow the body to avoid feeling some level of emotional and physical pain. As I discuss later in the book, the primary purpose of some alters is to be numb and therefore spare the host of pain.

Visual Disturbances Including Some Reports of Blindness

Many patients have alters with different visual acuity. Some need glasses all the time, some for reading, and other alters have perfect vision. I have often been able to identify which alter was present when treating someone with DID because he or she was wearing glasses or not. Putnam (1989, p. 66) reported visual disturbances ranging from "hysterical" diplopia to complete blindness in about one-fifth of patients with DID.

Psychogenic Deafness

Some alters are deaf. One of my patients had such an alter, who could only use sign language, which she claimed to have learned when another part worked in a day care that cared for several deaf children. (Unfortunately, the patient had learned to sign by spelling words, but she was a terrible speller. It definitely made for some challenging conversations!)

Limb Paralysis

Limb paralysis is not uncommon in patients with DID. A famous case was reported by psychiatrist Charles-Hubert-Antoine Despine in a monograph published in 1840 (Putnam, 1989). Despine was treating an 11-year-old Swiss girl named Estelle, whose symptoms evolved over time from an initial paralysis and exquisite sensitivity to touch, to an overt dual existence with a second personality that was able to walk, loved to play in the snow, and could not tolerate the sight of her mother. The 60-year-old Despine developed a close rapport with his young patient and was able to effect a cure through psychotherapy implicit in the variety of hydrotherapeutic and magnetic treatments he used.

More recently, Marilyn Van Derbur, Miss America in 1954, reported in her book, *Miss America by Day,* that she had been sexually abused by her father from age 5 to 18 years. She had no memory of these events, and had excelled in school and various activities. She married and had a little girl, and when her daughter turned the age that Marilyn had been when her abuse had started, Marilyn awoke one morning and was unable to walk. She remained paralyzed for quite a while. Doctors tried multiple approaches until finally someone began to explore issues related to possible abuse. When she began to recall the abuse, she recognized what she later called her day child and her night child. The night child took all the abuse, but the day child went to school and had no memory of the night child. As these memories came forth, the paralysis disappeared.

Motor Disturbances

Motor disturbances include involuntary repetitive body movements resembling tardive dyskinesia, often associated with rapid switching. This can be disturbing to witness and physically painful for the patient.

Cardiorespiratory Symptoms

Symptoms such as dyspnea, palpitations, chest pain, choking, or a sense of smothering are frequent, particularly when patients are processing the memories of their abuse. Patients who were forced to perform oral sex will have gagging sensations or pressure on their chest as their body remembers the feeling of the adult sitting on them. Again, however, before concluding this is a symptom of DID, always be certain that a physician has ruled out medical reasons for these symptoms.

Eating Disorders

Many patients with DID have eating disorders. One or more alters may have either anorexia or bulimia. Anorexia is an interesting symptom for these patients. Patients with anorexia generally hear a voice in their head telling them not to eat and not to listen to whoever may be trying to feed them. Although we know that there appear to be biological or genetic components to eating disorders, these behaviors are generally seen as an attempt to control something in a person's life. Starvation, taking diuretics and laxatives, and purging allow patients with DID to control what goes in and out of their bodies. Unfortunately, although they feel they are in control of something, they are truly spinning more and more out of control and causing self-harm. Anorexic behavior is seen in a high percentage of patients with DID, with a lesser percentage exhibiting bulimia (Putnam, 1989, p. 293).

Both bulimia and anorexia have addictive qualities. My patients have reported that feeling really hungry helps them remember they have some control; this feeling becomes somewhat addictive. The binge–purge cycle seen in bulimics works in much the same way as drugs and alcohol to reduce feelings of tension. Patients feel a rush after purging that allows them to remain numb to feelings of stress. Essentially, this adds to the dissociative element that is the core of DID.

It is important to remember that trying to "cure" the symptoms of bulimia or anorexia in these patients can be even more complicated than in a patient without DID who has an eating disorder. The patient may see removing the eating disorder as an attempt to remove or "kill off" a part. As long as that part remains, the alter with the symptoms is doing his or her job of protecting the patient from horrible memories and feelings. However, as the patient begins to recover as a whole, other parts, including the host, may begin to realize that those symptoms are no longer necessary. They know what happened and have begun processing the feelings. They begin to have a true sense of control over their lives.

Gastrointestinal and Reproductive System Symptoms

Gastrointestinal symptoms, especially irritable bowel syndrome, occur frequently in patients with DID. These patients often report episodes of nausea, vomiting, or diarrhea. Gastric pain may occur with viscerally remembered trauma. Patients also report pain in the reproductive system and, in particular, the vagina.

Sleep Difficulties, Nightmares, and Flashbacks

Many patients report difficulty sleeping. They are often anxious, afraid of the dark, or suffer nightmares. Anxiety tends to increase in most people at night when it is dark. Indeed, many patients with DID report increased flashbacks at night. Alters may get up and draw, write, have snacks, take showers, or watch television. Some may take the car keys and disappear for periods of time. This can be disturbing not only to the patient but to other family members as well.

Other Unusual Symptoms

In addition to the symptoms described thus far, unusual dermatological reactions, unexplained fevers, changes in blood sugar, or unusual responses to anesthesia have been reported with DID patients. One woman was a brittle diabetic when a child alter was out. However, as soon as any of the adult alters returned, her blood sugar stabilized. Although the host (usually the presenting patient) may take medications presumed to affect the entire body, this may not be the case. One alter may take the sleeping medicine, but then others wake up and wander about the house or actually go out during the night. It can be important therapeutically to remind the patient that all parts, inside and out, must take the medicine.

Aphonia is loss of the voice resulting from disease, injury to the vocal cords, or various psychological causes, such as hysteria. In patients with

DID, we may find one or more alters are essentially mute but are not preverbal infants and children. Some may use sign language as a form of communication.

Some patients also have significant negative reactions at certain times of year, especially the fall. Events such as Halloween, religious holidays, or certain religious celebrations appear to be triggers. This is because the abuse may have taken place during these specific times or in certain locations (such as a church when cult abuse is reported). Holidays, in general, frequently seen as family events, can be difficult times for many people, let alone those with DID. Treatment of patients with DID is generally long term. Thus, it may become clear that these patterns are recurring. It is helpful to be able to note these occurrences and plan for them. Additional sessions can be scheduled, memory work put on hold, alternate plans made, and coping skills reinforced so that these high-risk times may be better managed.

Many patients with DID have jobs that require responsibility. These individuals seem to have at least one strong alter that keeps younger and more troublesome alters away from work. I have worked with several nurses with DID. It is not surprising that some part of them would be in a helping profession. Other patients, however, have a history of frequent job changes. They may lead itinerant lives traveling the country in prolonged fugue states. There is often a pattern to their wanderings, with occurrences at particular times of the year or every few months, and we may begin to expect when we will hear from them again. Because of their long histories of abuse and cycles of self-abusive behaviors, these patients often have histories of revictimization as adults. Unfortunately, this is part of the legacy of childhood abuse.

six

Diagnosis

Diagnosis of dissociative identity disorder (DID) is not always easy. The key is knowing how and where to look for evidence on which to base your diagnosis. Putnam (1989) noted that Richard Kluft shared with him his diagnostic technique of deliberately extending the evaluation interview with a patient suspected of having DID. The theory is that it is difficult for a DID patient to keep from switching at some point during the stress of a prolonged interview. Because most insurance companies will not pay for such extended sessions and we often are not aware of the possible diagnosis until after a few sessions, it is frequently more practical to begin with traditional 50- to 60-minute sessions.

Often the first clue is that in consecutive sessions, you begin to hear information that is confusing, time lines are unclear, and the patient may seem confused when you refer to something said in a previous session. It is important to use the mindfulness and mentalizing stance described by Allen (2013). *Mentalizing* is the process through which we make sense of each other and ourselves, implicitly and explicitly, in terms of subjective states and mental processes. It is a profoundly social construct in the sense that we are attentive to the mental states of those we are with, physically or psychologically.

You may notice slightly different styles of dress or manners of speech. Pay attention to your own sense of confusion. It is probably an important sign of what your patient is feeling. It is also important to watch for defensive or compensatory maneuvers by the patients who seek to evade questions or divert parts of the inquiry. Ask about loss of time—amnesias related to periods of childhood or important life events. You might hear about a suicide attempt or hospitalization during one session and then get a confused look from the patient during the next session when you bring up the same topic. Ask patients about out-of-body experiences and feelings of depersonalization. Inquire whether others have called them a liar for attempts to cover up the fact that they cannot recall being places, talking to people, buying certain things, or rearranging things at home or work. Ask if they have a history of being late. Alters, wanting time "out," often interfere with getting to places on time. Many patients have diaries that can fill in gaps in history, but not all the alters know about the diaries or want to know what is in them. Although later in treatment you may hear the pronoun "we" as the patient describes something that they have done or experienced, it is far less common early in treatment.

It is important to rule out any organic causes for symptoms—including temporal lobe seizures, tumors, thyroid problems, or diabetes—and thus communication with patients' primary care doctor is important. Remember that even if the patient has DID, he or she may have physical problems as well, and you want to be certain not to chalk up every physical ailment to a physical manifestation of a psychological problem. One of my patients complained of incredible anxiety that left her drenched from sweating. Although it was initially seen as entirely related to anxiety, referral to her physician revealed a major thyroid problem that required surgical intervention. You also serve as an essential link to your patients' physician in explaining certain behaviors or their lack of apparent cooperation in medication management. In addition, a medical examination allows the physician to check for evidence of self-harm and old bruises from earlier injuries.

Traditional psychological tests are not terribly useful in the diagnosis of DID. The Minnesota Multiphasic Personality Inventory, Millon Clinical Multiaxial Inventory, or other traditional personality tests may be invalid or inconclusive if different alters are triggered to answer different questions. However, tests to assess level of dissociation can, at times, be helpful (Steinberg, 1994). A discussion of several of these follows.

Dissociative Experiences Scale

The Dissociative Experiences Scale (DES) was developed by Eve Bernstein, PhD, and Frank W. Putnam, MD, in 1986. It is a self-report measure consisting of 28 items and completed in about 10 minutes that can assist in identifying the frequency of certain dissociative symptoms. The overall DES score is obtained by adding up the 28 item scores and dividing by 28. This yields an overall score ranging from 0 to 100. DES is intended to be a screening test because only 17% of patients with scores over 30 will be diagnosed with DID. Patients with lower scores that are still above normal may have other posttraumatic conditions. It has shown to have good validity and reliability.

Somatoform Dissociative Questionnaire (Versions 20 and 5)

The Somatoform Dissociative Questionnaire is a 20-item questionnaire developed by Nijenhuis et al. (1996) that evaluates the severity of somatoform dissociation. Of sound psychometric quality, the items were derived from a pool of 75 items describing clinically observed somatoform dissociative symptoms that had appeared in clinical settings upon activation of particular dissociative parts of the personality and that could not be explained medically. The items pertain to both negative (e.g., analgesia) and positive dissociative (e.g., site-specific pain) phenomena.

These types of symptoms can be confusing to patients, especially when physicians tell them "there is nothing wrong with you." This questionnaire is a quick way to assess their symptoms. Again, however, remember that patients should be evaluated by medical personnel to rule out physical bases for symptoms. Just because a patient has DID does not mean he or she does not have gall bladder problems, thyroid issues, or heart problems, for example.

Dissociative Disorders Interview Schedule

The Dissociative Disorders Interview Schedule (DDIS) was developed by Ross and colleagues (Ross, Heber Norton, & Anderson, 1989) and is a highly structured interview that covers issues related to the diagnosis of DID as well as other psychological issues. It is based on the third revised edition of the *Diagnostic and Statistical Manual of Mental Disorders (DSM)* and can be administered in 30 to 45 minutes.

The DDIS is helpful in both diagnosing DID and ruling it out. Average scores in each of the 16 subsections based on a sample of patients with DID who have completed the inventory can be found in the appendix at the end of the article by Ross et al. (1989).

Structured Clinical Interview for *DSM–IV* Dissociative Disorders—Revised

The Structured Clinical Interview for *DSM–IV* Dissociative Disorders—Revised (SCID–D–R), developed by Steinberg (1994), is a highly structured and reliable interview instrument. Steinberg identified five core symptoms that she feels must be present to diagnose a patient with DID or DID not otherwise specified: dissociative amnesia, depersonalization, derealization, identity confusion, and identity alteration.

Confirming the Diagnosis

In the end, the only real confirmation of the presence of DID is when the clinician is able to meet alter personalities directly. This can be a fascinating experience. Early in my career, I was treating Casey, the 40-year-old nurse I mentioned earlier. She drove nearly an hour to see me for each visit. She acknowledged a history of sexual abuse and often would begin to cry when talking about the atrocities she had experienced. She asked if she could hold a teddy bear in my office and often seemed to let her nose run on the bear, a behavior that seemed a bit unusual for a nurse. I had never knowingly treated anyone with multiple personalities, although I regularly saw many individuals who had been abused. Frankly, if asked back then, I probably would have said I wasn't sure multiple personalities existed.

One day, shortly after Casey arrived, she said she had a bad headache. I asked her if she wanted to lie down on the couch for a few minutes. She did and shut her eyes. She lay there for what I felt was a long time and I began to think she had fallen asleep. I sat quietly wondering what to do and was surprised when she opened her eyes, looked confused and began talking to me. Her voice and mannerisms were that of a young child, around 3 or 4 years of age. It was difficult to deny the existence of the diagnosis at that point. I then learned about a previous hospitalization and consulted with the attending psychiatrist. Although he had been suspicious of the presence of alters, he had never met any and therefore could not make the diagnosis.

A review of the literature suggests that in about half of all cases, the first encounter with an alter is initiated by one or more of the alters who come out and identify themselves as being different from the patient (Putnam, 1989). Sometimes the contact is made in person, during a psychotherapy session, but contact may be made through a letter or phone call in which alters identify themselves as a friend of the patient's.

Communicating the Diagnosis

It is important to be gentle but direct when giving patients a diagnosis of DID. Although it can be scary for them to hear, it is often a relief that there is a logical explanation for their symptoms and recognition that they are not "crazy." Nonetheless, acceptance of the diagnosis of DID is often an ongoing issue, right down to the end of therapy and integration. There are often alters who really struggle with the idea that there are other alters and are terrified of simply dying if the patient improves in treatment. In some ways, this can be seen as a form of resistance to psychotherapy. However, over time, there is generally an acceptance of most, if not all, the alters.

A word of caution: Avoid searching for the presence of alters through hypnosis. We do not want to create iatrogenic outcomes— situations in which the patient appears to have alters on the basis of suggestions or actions by the therapist. If alters are present, they will make themselves known. You will meet them, or another part may tell you about them. On the other hand, it is important to recognize that hypnotic phenomena occur commonly in most dissociative populations and play a significant role in their psychopathology (Kluft, 2012). High hypnotizability is commonly encountered in traumatized individuals whose conditions become the most chronic. Kluft pointed out that highly hypnotizable people are vulnerable to slipping into alert trances in which, with eyes wide open, they manifest many of the qualities of the more formally and traditionally hypnotized individuals. They may demonstrate a reduction in their alertness and activity of their critical intellect, a toleration of mutually incompatible perceptions without reacting to their incompatibility, the intensification of affect, rapid mobilization of transference phenomena, and an increased responsiveness to suggestions. As a result, it is important to be aware of these phenomena and trained in understanding and in the use of hypnosis. I discuss this further in Chapter 8, which focuses on treatment.

Mental Status Evaluation

The following summary of what you might observe in a mental status evaluation of a patient with DID is adapted from Putnam (1989). Note that the changes noted here can occur within a single session or during separate sessions over days, weeks, months, and, in some cases, years. Generally, little switching occurs during an initial session. Different alters may later appear for complete sessions, however. Most patients with DID have spent a great deal of time and effort hiding what is actually happening to them and may try hard to hide this from a psychotherapist until they feel safe in treatment.

Appearance

During your evaluation, pay attention to changes in facial appearance, expressions, posture, and mannerisms that occur within a single session. Handedness and habits such as needing eyeglasses may change within a short period of time. Style of dress, grooming, general appearance, and mannerisms may change dramatically from session to session. One alter may arrive in a business suit, another looking more like a "hooker." One colleague reported that she regularly saw a patient in her office who was always well dressed and put together. One day at the supermarket, she ran into the same woman looking unkempt and completely disheveled.

Speech

Watch for changes in rate, pitch, accent, loudness, vocabulary, and even the language a patient speaks. Note the use of idiosyncratic expressions and or profanity within single and across several sessions.

Motor Processes

Rapid blinking, eyelid fluttering, marked eye rolls, tics, twitches, startle reactions, shudders, and facial grimaces often accompany the switch between alter personalities. Sometimes dramatic full-body "struggles" are noticed as individual alters fight to come out or the host tries to prevent this from happening. This can be unnerving for the psychotherapist, or anyone else, to watch. It can actually be painful for the patient to experience as well. It is helpful to develop a relaxation technique or process to help the patient during the switching. Again, however, it is essential that you, the psychotherapist, are not bringing on the switching. Only after observing how the switching is occurring should you discuss ways that could make things easier, if necessary.

With Ellen, we found a way for the host to disappear inside to a safe rock on the beach. Using a form of relaxation and guided imagery, she was able to leave a door ajar as she went inside so the part coming out would have an easier exit. The host informed me that she had been fighting any alter wanting to come out because she was not ready to have contact with the other parts. As treatment progressed, we were able to use this technique to help alters begin to make contact with each other as they switch, interact, and break down the barriers of communication.

Thought Processes

The thought processes of patients with DID may appear to be non-sequential and illogical at times. Associations may appear to be loose, and patients may appear to block or lose their train of thought. This is most prominent with rapid switching or "revolving-door crises" in which we see the "word salad" effect. This occurs when several alters are trying to "be out" and speak at the same time, and what is actually heard makes no sense as bits and pieces of each alter's sentences come through. The appearance of a thought disorder does not seem to persist beyond the crisis. Patients may report a long history of lying to cover up the fact that they have no memory of being somewhere or doing something or saying something. They may also report a sense of total confusion after a revolving-door episode has occurred. In these situations, it can be helpful to let the system know that you want to hear from everyone who wants to talk, but it must be done in an orderly fashion. Someone on the inside can be appointed to decide who will speak first or to try to determine what everyone on the inside is trying to say.

Hallucinations and Delusions

As noted earlier, auditory or visual hallucinations and delusions seem to be present, but this may not always be the case. The patient may report voices arguing about the patient or what the patient should do. The voices are generally within the head. Voices may be both positive and negative. After the correct diagnosis is made, patients may say that, because of the voices in their head, they have always thought they were "crazy." Once a diagnoses is made, they may begin to learn to listen to the inside voices rather than just to block them out.

Intellectual Functioning

Short-term memory, orientation, calculations and fund of knowledge are generally intact for these patients. In fact, many patients with DID are quite intelligent. Long-term memory may show deficits. However, formal tests, such as an IQ test, may not be valid depending on which alter has taken the test or even different parts of the test. Some alters may be triggered by certain questions or pictures on the test. IQ tests do not solely measure intellectual functioning. Rather, they provide a sample of behavior and often serve as a projective measure for the clinician as well. In terms of long-term memory, as treatment progresses, different alters may help to create a life events timeline to help the host regain a sense of self.

Judgment

Patients may display rapid fluctuations in appropriateness of behavior and judgment. These shifts often occur along an age dimension (i.e., from adult to childlike behavior). Casey generally had excellent judgment and certainly was always appropriate at her job. However, her teenage son sometimes triggered her own adolescent alter. On one occasion, an alter reported that her son was behaving badly, and she ended up sitting on top of him, straddling him with her legs as she lectured him. At the time, she said she felt that was the only way to control him. It was her teen alter that had done this, and we had a long discussion about how this behavior was sexually inappropriate with a teenage boy. The older parts agreed to monitor this behavior.

Insight

The personality presenting for treatment most of the time may not be aware of the existence of alternate personalities. However, many of the alters on the inside are aware of at least a few other parts. Some of the alters have an incredible insight into others, including the psychotherapist. They have had to develop a keen sense of situational awareness to survive, and this can, at times, be a bit disconcerting to the clinician. They will be aware of when you are not fully present in the session. They will call you on your distraction and may ask prying and personal questions. They are not generally trying to be difficult. They are trying to assess the situation and stay safe. It is important for the therapist to think carefully about responses to these types of personal questions. Honesty is important, but that doesn't mean you must reveal personal information. An honest response can be a statement that this therapy is about the patient, followed by a discussion of why that information is important for the patient to know.

seven

Types and Roles of Alter Personalities

Putnam (1989) described alters as "discrete states of consciousness organized around a prevailing affect, sense of self (including body image) with a limited repertoire of behaviors, and a set of state dependent memories" (p. 103). Kluft (1984) described an alter personality as:

> *An entity with a firm, persistent and well founded sense of self, and a characteristic and consistent pattern of behavior and feelings in response to given stimuli. It must have a range of functions, a range of emotional responses and a significant history of its own existence.* (p. 23)

Some authors emphasize the importance of personality and personality fragments with dissociative identity disorder (DID) patients (Putnam, 1989, p. 104). This can be difficult to distinguish, and I have found it appears to make little practical difference during treatment.

I also have found that although it is clearly important to know which alters exist, I rarely spend time counting the number of personalities, as if somehow "the more, the merrier" or "the more, the sicker." For example, Kelly, a 35-year-old woman with DID, spoke of the Indians that kept her from doing things. She talked about them as if they were an army. They made a lot of noise that often gave her headaches. As treatment progressed, I learned that although there were a lot of them (I never knew how many), they were all 11 years old, and making noise served to sabotage her treatment. We dealt with them as a single group of "scared kids." I suggested that the other inside parts could help to build a fort or tree house in a wooded area where they could play, away from treatment. The patient thought that was a good idea, had an internal meeting (more about these later), a tree house was built, and the Indians disappeared. They were never formally integrated but also never returned. They apparently integrated spontaneously when they no longer needed to serve as a distraction. They actually were more like personality fragments that had no true autonomy. So, although keeping track of numbers is not essential, it is important to identify the key players and typical types of alters.

It is also important to recall that alter personalities generally arise as a defensive response to what is perceived as overwhelming trauma (Kluft, 1984). Over time, alters may come to acquire a significant degree of autonomy and investment in their separateness (Kluft, 1984). They may change from performing psychologically defensive tasks, such as screening out or absorbing unbearable experiences, to having their own independent objectives, which conflict with those of the individual as a whole. They may acquire new functions or relinquish old ones. The psychotherapist must learn what alters perceive to be their current role in the system. Often, for the individual to heal, the alters have to accept a new "job description" that utilizes their particular skills. For example, the psychotherapist might encourage the "mouthy teen" who acted out by drinking to help the others speak up for themselves. As they begin to feel they are heard, they may voluntarily give up some of their anger, which is destructive to the system, and help the system process appropriate anger toward the actual abusers. Sometimes it is helpful to have the patient draw who and which alters are in her head. The drawings can reveal alters who have not yet emerged and may indicate the strength or position of an alter within the system. Some patients draw shadows or parts that they see inside but can't fully describe.

Types of Alter Personalities

A review of the literature shows consistency among the types of alters that frequently present in patients with DID. However, alters do not seem to have any consistent hierarchical order. At different times, different parts take center stage and seem to occupy greater parts of the patient's internal and external worlds.

The Host

There is always the *host*, the one who has executive control over the greatest percentage of time. This may not be the birth individual. It is the host who usually presents initially for treatment and is identified as the patient before the diagnosis of DID. Sometimes the host is actually a social facade in which several alters agree to pass as one.

The host often presents in distress. He or she may feel overwhelmed, depressed, anxious, and confused; report having headaches; and is frequently unaware of any of the other parts. Stern (1984) noted that it is more often the case that the host denies the existence of alter selves than the alter personalities deliberately hide themselves from the host.

Child Personalities

There are always a number of *child personalities*, each holding specific memories of traumatic events. These children often appear for the first time during some horrific event that the birth child could not have tolerated. Sometimes, one child alter was present for a part of a particular event, and another child alter appeared to handle the rest of it. These memories will eventually be told bit by bit with the different children contributing to the whole history. These children are generally frozen at that age and point of development until late in treatment when they may blend or grow into the adult before integration. Some of the children may be nonverbal, some may just cry, and some may initially see the psychotherapist as an abuser. Often two or more of the children appear to be friends and play together or help each other. The children may also look up to older alters for protection. Teen and adult alters can be used successfully during treatment to help soothe the younger ones, especially after they have shared their part of the story. I have frequently encouraged older parts to sit and read to or rock or hold younger parts that need soothing. This is generally a successful technique. There may be quite a few child alters—more than adult ones. They can cause problems because they are usually lacking the judgment or skills to handle certain situations into which they emerge. However, for the most part, adult alters keep young alters from driving cars or showing up at work. Some patients have told me that they woke up to find a younger part sitting in the driver's seat and was either unable to reach the pedals or feeling confused about what to do. Also, some younger teens do occasionally take control of the car and have accidents.

Persecutor Personalities

At least half of patients with DID have alters who see themselves in diametric conflict with the host. These are called *persecutors.* Sometimes they represent introjects of the original abuser (Putnam, 1986). An *introject* in psychoanalytical terms is the process in which the subject replicates in itself behaviors, attributes, or other fragments of the surrounding world, especially of other subjects. Others may have evolved from the original helper person into current persecutors. They may actively try to undermine treatment. A natural tendency for psychotherapists is to try to avoid the persecutors or to silence them in some way. This can be a major clinical error. They are an important part of the DID system and must be dealt with accordingly. Otherwise, they have power over you, the psychotherapist, and the other alters will remain terrorized. They can be won over, and once they know that you are not afraid of them, they may actually help in treatment. Remember, the system created all the alters to help it survive in some way. In their anger, the alters often contain much of the energy and strength that the DID patient needs to survive and improve. Many patients who have been abused have incorporated some of the behaviors of the abuser into themselves, just as many perpetrators of abuse may have some victim behaviors or emotions in them. Their energy is often connected to threatening anyone trying to tell the secrets.

Recall Ellen, the 38-year-old woman I described earlier. She had a male alter whom she described as an "entity." It "was" the grandfather who had been her primary abuser. She could not accept that *he* could actually be a part of her. *He* would threaten to harm her and the other alters. At times, *he* would take control and do things like go out on her porch and smoke a cigar. After a difficult session during which my patient talked about her anger toward the grandfather, I received a phone call from this alter threatening me to leave my patient alone and telling me *he* was in charge. The voice was deep and intimidating. I finally was able to convince *him* not to hurt anyone at least until *he* met with me in the next session. When *he* arrived I really was a bit taken aback and somewhat intimidated. *He* walked and spoke in a masculine style. *He* promptly sat in my chair and made a lewd comment about a picture of a little girl on my wall. No wonder the host was afraid of *him*.

After a while I was able to talk to *him* about his relationship with the host. *He* insisted that *he* had never hurt her as a child and that *he* actually loved her. But *he* was tired of being bad-mouthed. *He* bought her clothes and ice cream when she was little. *He* had been the one to teach her about sex and often took control of the body when she had sex with her husband. *He* decided *he* really didn't want to do that anymore because he was an old man and would give that job back to her. *He* also was able to contract not to hurt the host or any other part, inside or out.

We discussed his strengths and ways he could help the host. The patient said she felt much more present and relaxed during sex with her husband after that session. This alter showed up a few times after that, but generally for brief periods. As treatment was winding down, however, the patient reported feeling his presence. I invited that part to talk with me. When he appeared, he told me that he felt he was losing control of the body, and this was upsetting to him. He agreed not to hurt any of the parts as long as I would not deny his existence. In fact, only after that session was the patient able to understand that this part had been around from the beginning and did carry a lot of physical and emotional energy. She was able to talk about some negative things she knew about her grandfather's childhood and began to work to accept that this part was not a sign of possession but an early attempt on her part to cope with the trauma.

Suicidal Personalities

Frequently there are one or more suicidal personalities. The fifth edition of the *Diagnostic and Statistical Manual of Mental Disorders* (*DSM–5*; American Psychiatric Society, 2013) notes that more than 70% of outpatients with DID have attempted suicide. Multiple attempts are common, and other self-injurious behavior is frequent. Assessment of suicide risk may be complicated when there is amnesia for past suicidal behavior or when the presenting identity does not feel suicidal and was unaware that other dissociated identities do.

These parts can truly complicate treatment. The therapist cannot take these parts lightly. Some can be trusted to make a no-suicide contract (NSC) with the therapist, but this is not always the case. In fact, the existing research does not support the use of such contracts as a method for preventing suicide. Nor does having a suicide contract with a patient protect clinicians from malpractice litigation in the event of a patient suicide (Lewis, 2007). In the one case (*Stepakoff v. Kantar*) known to have addressed the issue of NSCs directly, the court found that "NSCs cannot stand alone and must be a part of a broader assessment of lethality" (Miller, Jacobs, & Gutheil, cited in Hyldahl & Richardson, 2009). Parties to any contract must be deemed to be legally competent. Regarding patients who have a mental illness or who experience extreme levels of agitation, anxiety, or depression, there is certainly the potential for the patient to be deemed functionally or affectively incompetent to enter into any type of binding agreement (Simon, 1999).

So what does all this mean for the therapist treating a patient with DID who has one or more alters that are suicidal? First of all, the therapist must do a thorough assessment of lethality. One must then establish a safety plan. This includes a discussion of the options patients have at their disposal before and instead of hurting themselves. If necessary, family or other support members may need to be contacted, and, on occasion, hospitalization must occur. This type of discussion must include all the alters and all of the concerns to be documented. Even when this is done, it is difficult to know, especially early in treatment, whether there is a part that has not presented himself or herself and is not participating in the discussions.

Appendix C provides recommendations put forth by Hyldahl and Richardson (2009) for incorporating no-harm contracts into the treatment process.

One of my patients, Jane, had several alters who would call me from a pay phone and tell me of a suicide plan. When I was able to locate the patient and on occasion hospitalize her, another alter would come out to talk with the staff and convince them she was perfectly fine and should be released to go home. Jane seemed to create chaos wherever she went. She would leave my office and go hide under a chair at the psychiatrist's office down the street. I was unable to establish any type of safety plan with her. I clearly could not trust her to keep herself safe. On one occasion when I was able to convince the hospital to keep her, she became romantically involved with a staff member. They ran away together, left the state, and both ended up being arrested. Ultimately, I had to discharge her from my care because I felt we had no therapeutic relationship and I could not establish any safety for her. Her psychiatrist continued to treat her. Jane ultimately committed suicide about a year and a half later. It was a difficult decision for me to discharge Jane. She is the only patient with DID that I have ever discharged. I still believe I really had no choice. Therapy was simply chaos, and I made sure she retained a treating doctor. I believe that sometimes, no matter what we do, if someone remains truly intent on killing him- or herself, there is little we can do to prevent it. But it never feels good.

Sometimes we trigger suicidal ideation in alters without realizing what has occurred. When I first met Kelly, she had been referred by another patient. She had been fired from her job and was very depressed. As I did a fairly routine intake, I asked her about difficulty with issues of intimacy. She kind of nodded and didn't say too much. She told me she was going out of state and would call after she returned. A few weeks later, I received a call from a psychiatrist in another state. Kelly had made a serious suicide attempt when she had arrived there and had been hospitalized. Kelly did come back to my office on her return and told me that my question about intimacy had really scared her. She thought I could read her thoughts or see into her and knew about all her abuse and fears. She felt so vulnerable that she had wanted to die and attempted suicide. It wasn't for many months that I realized she had DID. As we talked about what had happened at the beginning of therapy, she told me that although a part of her had been terrified by my questions related to her issues with intimacy, a part of her was relieved that I might understand her fears.

Internal Self-Helper

Fortunately, there is generally a part that is called the *internal self-helper* (ISH). These alters are present in approximately 50% to 80% of DID patients and are generally extremely helpful. They may be rather passive and emotionless but often provide information and insights. They may go by names, such as the "Wise One" or the "Strong One," or they may have a more typical name, such as Linda or Helen. In women patients, the ISH may be a male. They can frequently help nurture the younger parts, control teens or other parts that are acting out, and be responsible for maintaining communication with the psychotherapist and monitoring suicidal behaviors and contracts. I have called on the ISHs on many occasions when I needed to know what was happening inside the system and wanted help in stabilizing it. Once aware of their existence, I have been able to ask to speak with them when on the phone trying to handle a crisis in another alter. I can then determine if we can keep the patient safe without any extreme intervention such as a hospitalization. ISH parts are particularly helpful in developing safety plans. Putnam (1989) noted that it is not uncommon for a suicidal or homicidal personality to take an overdose of medication and then for a protector personality to emerge and call 911. The homicidal alter falsely believes it can kill another alter but not him- or herself.

Teenagers

Generally, there are *teenagers* among the alters who can be mouthy and at times drink alcohol, use drugs, or act out sexually. However, once you gain their trust and they see you that understand the purpose of their behavior was to numb the host so that he or she could survive, they can be helpful, both on the inside and out. As noted earlier, they often hold the younger parts, read them stories, or play with them. They also can stand up to people who continue to try to hurt the others. Unfortunately, they often feel like no one likes them and feel bad about themselves. It is important to make it clear that you are aware they acted out to try to protect the birth personality from being hurt in some way. I generally find the teen parts to be energetic and interesting and that they want to feel loved and accepted.

Cross-Gender Personalities

Another interesting phenomenon is the presence of *cross-gender* alters, which occur in approximately 50% of patients with DID. They may be introjects of the abuser or may be attempts at finding someone "stronger' to handle things. However, it may also be an explanation for the unisex look of many patients with DID. Many patients are unsure of their sexuality after being badly abused. Males abused by men often wonder if they are gay. They question whether their abuser saw something in them about which they were unaware. They will ask me questions such as, "Why did he pick me? Do I look gay? Or do I make others think I am gay?" even if in their heart they truly believe they are heterosexual. Women who have been badly abused sometimes choose a homosexual lifestyle in an attempt to find a nurturing partner and avoid the more intrusive sexuality they experienced at the hands of male abusers. As they begin to recover from the abuse, they may want to explore their sexuality and try engaging in sexual contact with a male. This can be a scary but important part of their treatment. It is important to support patients in an open discussion of what truly makes them comfortable. Interestingly, male patients often have a female alter that represents the good mother, even if their abuser was a woman.

Promiscuous Alters

There are often alters who are promiscuous or who handle the sexual relationship with a spouse or partner. It is not unusual to hear that a woman with DID was outgoing and sexually available before the marriage, but after the wedding avoids sexual behavior. It is as if the sex, now, back in the family, represents the trauma of incest again.

Administrators

Administrator alters generally show up in the workplace. They are organized, competent, and professional. They are generally the alters that aid the patient in earning a living and other important jobs, such as running the household.

Other Types of Alters

Other types of alters include *autistic or handicapped* parts, those with *special talents* or who *speak a foreign language* unknown to the other alters, and those who deny the presence of any pain, sometimes referred to as *anesthetic* or *analgesics*.

My patient Ellen had a thyroid condition that led to feelings of anxiety and panic. She would get extremely sweaty and have a racing heart. Initially the psychiatrist felt it was simply anxiety. She prescribed anxiolytics, which Ellen tended to overuse. When she started working, she would have to go to the restroom and try to cool off with cold water. Ultimately, Ellen was diagnosed with a thyroid nodule. A specialist confirmed the diagnosis and noted that her symptoms were typical for someone with that diagnosis. She had a strong family history of thyroid conditions, including Graves' disease and Hashimoto's disease. Interestingly, she had an alter whose purpose was to step in when Ellen was overwhelmed with physical symptoms. This alter slipped easily in and out and was difficult to detect. However, Ellen reported that sometimes she "just felt better." As treatment progressed, Ellen told me she felt the presence of someone that seemed to help her. She didn't feel threatened by her and knew she had mentioned her in the past. Ultimately that part came out during a session and helped me understand her role. She noted that she simply felt numbness, not pounding, in her chest and did not sweat. She also told me that she could not sustain the numbness for too long and would have to go back inside. She was also afraid that Ellen would ignore her physical symptoms if she thought there was a part that felt no pain. She worried that Ellen would simply feel crazy and ignore appropriate treatment.

There may be some *imitations* and *imposters* just to confuse the psychotherapist. Sometimes alters, as noted previously, will be identified as *demons* or *spirits*, more often seen in patients from rural areas or those with extreme fundamentalist religious beliefs. In the case of Ellen's grandfather alter, which I described earlier in the chapter, she often felt as if he was a demon or the actual spirit of her grandfather, returned from the dead.

The original person or *birth personality* is often not seen until much later in treatment. They are sometimes described as "sleeping" or even "dead" because he or she seems to have little knowledge of the abuse, and the system is really not ready for the birth personality to hear the horrors of what occurred. Remember, the alters developed as a defense for the birth child so she or he would not have to deal with the abuse.

The various alters have differing awareness of the others. One of the major tasks of treatment is to make available to the entire system of personalities the knowledge and secrets held by the others. This generalization of knowledge gradually erodes the need for separateness and begins the movement toward resolution and integration.

Early in Casey's treatment, she showed me pictures she had drawn during a previous hospitalization. One picture was of a tombstone with "RIP Catherine" written on it. Catherine was the name given to her at birth. However, she never wanted to use it. Only much later in treatment was an alter able to tell me that the system was really angry at Catherine. After all, if she had not been born, the rest of them would never have been abused.

Manifestations of Switching

The manifestations of switching vary among patients with DID. Some are quite dramatic and involve a strong physical response, as the alters literally struggle to take over the body. At other times, the change will be observed with eyes rolling back, blank stares, staring at the rug or ceiling, or complaints of severe headache followed by a closing of the eyes. I have seen changes occur when the patient removed her glasses and could now see perfectly well, although other alters could not. Sometimes, however, these changes are quite subtle, especially when alters are of similar ages. You might simply feel like something has changed but you are not really sure. Certainly, you could note aloud that "something seems different." Early in treatment, the patient might ignore your comment or deny a change. As time goes on, however, that part might identify itself, or you can ask more direct questions. Although I previously noted that it is inappropriate to use hypnosis for a "search and find" of alters, be aware that patients frequently go through a self-hypnosis as alters go in and out.

Different alters may have different physiologic sensitivities, allergic reactions, or responses to alcohol. For example, one might do the drinking, and the other wakes up with a hangover, feeling confused.

Of course, patients do not switch only in session. They switch throughout the day and in different situations. I have had patients report that they have been "put to sleep" during surgery and in the middle of the operation another alter awoke completely unaffected by the anesthesia! Clearly it is a good idea that physicians and surgeons be informed of the presence of this disorder and the possibility that this might occur before any surgical procedure. Otherwise, the patient's life could be at risk.

eight

Treatment

Treatment with dissociative identity disorder (DID) patients is in some ways similar to good treatment with most other patients, especially those who have experienced severe trauma. There are, however, some differences and some "tricks of the trade" that are extremely important.

The guidelines for the treatment of DID from the International Society for the Study of Dissociation (2011) state the importance of not creating counter-therapeutic and iatrogenic outcomes. These guidelines recommend that psychotherapists not treat any alternate identity as more important than any other, not create additional alternate identities by asking the patient to name them when there may be none, not suggest that alternate identities function more elaborately or autonomously than they are already, not ask the patient to ignore or get rid of alternate identities, and not play favorites with any of the alternate identities. Instead, the psychotherapist must help to foster the idea that alternate identities represent adaptive attempts to cope with the many problems that the DID patient experiences. Hence, the alternate identities can be helped to find more adaptive ways to solve problems rather than using solutions that are dysfunctional, unsafe, or problematic.

In a survey of practices and recommended treatment interventions of DID (Brand et al., 2012), it was found that highly experienced therapists recommended a carefully staged treatment consisting of three phases. In the initial phase, they advocated emphasizing skill building in development and maintenance of safety from dangerousness to self and others and other high-risk behaviors, such as emotion regulation, impulse control, interpersonal effectiveness, grounding, and containment of material. In addition, they recommended specific trauma-focused cognitive therapy to address trauma-based cognitive distortions. They uniformly recommended identifying and working with dissociated self-states beginning early in treatment. They advised the use of exposure or controlled abreaction techniques, modified so as not to overwhelm these patients, balanced with core foundational interventions for the middle stage. The last stage of treatment was less clearly delineated and more individualized. Unification of the self-states (formal integration) appears to occur in only a minority of patients with DID.

Courtois (2012) identified three stages that are measured in terms of mastery of skills and healing tasks, not in terms of time:

Stage 1: Alliance-building, safety, skill building, self-management

Stage 2: Trauma processing, deconditioning, resolution

Stage 3: Self and relational development

These phases are really important to ensuring the patient's physical and emotional safety and promoting the development of new and lifelong coping skills.

Principles of Treatment

Throughout these stages, it is important to keep in mind what I have found to be 12 basic principles for treatment. These are consistent with the existing literature.

1. **Maintain and secure firm boundaries.** Patients with DID may consciously or unconsciously push boundaries. Often their lives are in chaos, and, if you are not careful, they can pull you into their world. They may miss or be late for appointments, try to extend a session, or call during non–office hours, for example. Although it helps to have some flexibility with these patients, the more structured you are, the better it is for everyone. If you are not clear and boundaries are fuzzy, you will add to their chaos. Be clear about your cancellation policy, and don't be afraid to charge for missed sessions. Decide how

long and how often you are willing to talk between sessions to avoid a crisis without charging. Let them know these policies upfront, and enforce them consistently (although not rigidly).

2. **Focus on achieving mastery and emphasize patients' accomplishments.** Let them know when you see their strengths. They actually have so many! Interestingly, they often don't want to talk about their strengths and become uncomfortable with compliments. Later in Kelly's treatment, I commented one day that although I knew she was involved in a lot of positive activities outside of treatment, she never seemed to want to discuss them. She clearly pointed out to me that she was managing things outside of treatment pretty well, but she did not want to waste time talking about those things. She wanted to use her time and money to complain and talk about the things that were irritating her. She made her point! I realized I was thinking of my own desires to hear of her progress rather than trusting she was using her therapy sessions based on her needs.

3. **Establish and maintain a strong therapeutic alliance.** Without a solid alliance, treatment cannot be accomplished. A common mistake made by inexperienced psychotherapists is the tendency to rush into dealing with trauma memories. Watch for signs that the patient is feeling overwhelmed or pulling back from treatment by missing or cancelling appointments.

4. **Deal with buried traumatic events and affect unless there are contraindications for intense memory work** (discussed in more detail later in the chapter). Not every single traumatic event needs to be discussed. Nor can they be. After a while, some generalization will occur.

5. **Reduce separateness and conflict among alters.** Emphasize their collaboration and identification with each other so their separateness becomes redundant.

6. **Work to achieve congruence of perception.** Because their reality is often confused, it is important to be clear in your communications. Sometimes I find myself asking, "Was that clear, or did it sound too much like psychobabble?" When I ask the

question, I already know by the look on the patient's face that something I said was either too complicated or convoluted. Patients truly appreciate your own recognition that you were not clear.

7. **Treat all personalities evenhandedly, consistently, and with respect, and try to determine the strength of each alter.** Do not ignore an alter because it is annoying or even scary. I mentioned earlier that at times, some psychotherapists find it a helpful technique to map or have patients draw pictures of who the alters are and where they exist in the system. This can be modified as new alters emerge, a common occurrence in treatment. It may also help the psychotherapist understand the degree of power or control of any particular alter based on the size and placement in the picture.

8. **Restore basic shattered assumptions.** For example: "life is meaningful . . . I can see myself in a positive light." This involves changing cognitive distortions. Statements such as the following may be helpful: "Based on what you and I have discussed and been through together, I am reasonably certain that you will, despite your fears, come through this all right." So often patients with DID see only the negative parts of themselves, or simply see themselves as damaged or sick, possibly because this was the label that their abusers gave them. Or it may be their role in their family of origin. When appropriate, remind them that despite their multiplicity, they are really doing a great job of parenting or of managing their work and family. Acknowledge the creativity of even developing parts and point out that DID is truly an amazing and resilient response to trauma.

9. **Minimize avoidable overwhelming experiences.** This includes, pacing the psychotherapy and making sure the patient leaves your office with an adult alter in control. As we previously discussed, patients may need to sit in the waiting room for a while after session. In case they have gone into an alert trance or a fugue state, they may be less alert for safe driving. Do not begin discussing traumatic material at the end of a session. And if

you are in doubt about whether the patient is ready to tolerate something, wait!

10. **Model, teach, and reinforce responsibility.** Although patients with DID may have more problems with being on time, missing appointments, and needing between-session support, and psychotherapists may need to have increased tolerance for some of these behaviors, some things must be clear. Boundaries keep you and your patient safe. Don't compromise what you know is good treatment in an attempt to "help" your patient. These patients can be very needy. As psychotherapists, we want to reach out and help. We want to be available and helpful. Many clinicians argue over whether we are reparenting our patients. Clearly we cannot be their parent, but we can role-model good parenting techniques, which involves not only acceptance but also good and clear boundaries that keep everyone safe.

11. **Take an active, warm, and sensitive but structured stance.** You need to know when to be quiet and when to be more active. Generally speaking, patients with DID want you to participate, not simply ask, "How does that make you feel?" On the other hand, I learned an important lesson about timing and being quiet. Kelly, one of my earlier patients with DID, would often seem lost and remain quiet when I asked certain questions. Because she rarely made eye contact with me early in treatment, I sometimes thought maybe she had not heard me or misunderstood the question. A few times I either repeated the question or tried to ask it in another way. One day she asked me quite directly to "please shut up." She then proceeded to tell me that when I asked questions, she sometimes got responses from many different alters inside simultaneously. She had to sort through all their responses before she could answer me, and my talking simply interrupted the process! Believe me, I learned a lot from this amazing woman.

12. **Address and correct cognitive errors and distortions.** Kelly, the woman I just described, would not look me in the eye for years because she was sure I would see the "shit" she felt was in her

eyes. Patients often feel they were responsible for their abuser's behaviors. Patients have told me they were certain they must have a certain smell that their abuser could not resist. This can be a difficult distortion to correct, even in patients who were abused but do not have DID. A major distortion in patients with DID is that no one can really be trusted. Clearly, and in all reality, there were a lot of people in their lives who could not be trusted. Over time, if you are careful, they may discover safety in your office and begin to realize that at least you can be trusted to do what you say you will do and will make every attempt to keep your office a safe place. A word of advice here: I regularly ask patients, especially those who have been abused, to tell me why they feel safe or unsafe I my office. It is important that they learn to trust their gut to know when and where they really are safe.

Hypnosis can be an excellent technique for relief of chronic pain, headaches associated with "switching" of alters, and general calming of the system. It would be hard to work with patients with DID without having a good understanding of hypnosis, when to use it, and when to work to keep the patient present. As treatment progresses, I often work with patients to stay present as they communicate with the inside system. This is an important and early step (although often difficult at first) in helping them utilize techniques other than dissociation when they are stressed or need to get information from other parts.

Contraindications for Intense Memory Work

It is extremely important to know when to avoid memory work and to make stabilization the primary goal. Be cautious or avoid memory work altogether under the following conditions:

1. The patient is suicidal.
2. The patient has been unable to find healthy methods to self-soothe when emotionally upset. The ability to sooth oneself is more difficult when an internal self-helper has not been identified or is not present.
3. The patient does not have a safe place to live. For example, she continues to live with perpetrators of the abuse or individuals who deny the reality of the abuse.

4. The patient, or his or her support system, is currently dealing with other life crises or other serious situations, including health issues.
5. The patient is actively abusing substances.
6. A strong and trusting therapeutic relationship has not been established.
7. The patient is having ongoing contact with abusers.
8. The psychotherapist is going on vacation.
9. Other important events, such as holidays or weddings, are about to happen.
10. The patient has been erratic in attending sessions.

When it has been determined that a particular individual cannot tolerate intensive memory work the following guidelines for supportive or short-term treatment are recommended (Steele, 1991):

1. Safety must be the first priority.
2. Aim to consolidate ego strength by teaching mindfulness and grounding techniques. Ego strength is the ability of the ego to effectively deal with the demands of the entire personality and cope with emotional stress.
3. Help them focus on improvement of their current life. This may involve case management, change in living arrangements, and vocational rehabilitation, for example.
4. Contain and suppress memories.
5. Focus on affect management. Teach them what to do when they feel overwhelmed by their feelings. Help them to "decatastrophize."
6. Normalize their dissociation for them and help them accept their internal world. For example, they may hear voices in their head, but they don't always have to pay attention to them, unless there is an issue of safety.
7. Encourage them to focus on the here and now.
8. Provide psychoeducation about abuse.
9. Use medication management to stabilize mood and symptoms.
10. Teach short-term stress reduction techniques such as relaxation and exercise.

Techniques for Management of Traumatic Memories

Most patients with DID will be a bit leery of talking about trauma they experienced. After all, they developed alters so they wouldn't have to think about or remember the bad experiences. Alters often feel they are stuck in the abuse. They believe that it is actually happening again. They need constant reminders that this is now and the abuse was then. Abreaction, an emotional release or discharge after recalling a painful experience that has been repressed because it was intolerable, is a routine part of trauma work. However, some psychotherapists encourage this emotional release to be processed as if the original trauma was actually occurring and feel they have to provide extra long sessions to allow the patient to process all of their feelings. I believe this is painful and unnecessary. If the therapist uses techniques to help the patient process what happened, while at the same time understanding that they do not have to relive every moment of every emotion, I believe patients can achieve appropriate release while remaining safe and less traumatized. The emotion can be processed and contained. The patient will be able to recall the memories but will have lost the intense emotional charge. Steele (1991), in a workshop presentation, identified a number of excellent techniques discussed, in the following sections, to help minimize the pain involved when revisiting the trauma. Patients are generally in a state of autohypnosis when they are recalling memories. Although, as I have discussed at several points in this text, hypnosis is not used as a "search-and-find mission" to look for abuse, hypnotic induction techniques can be used to give the patient safety suggestions.

Permissive Amnesia

Tell your patients, "It's okay to remember only what you need and what is useful to you." This gives them permission rather than prohibiting them from doing something. It allows them to have the control. As treatment progresses, the inside parts generally hear more of what is being said on the outside, and they seem to process more of the material between sessions. Some describe this process as beginning to feel the memories as their own rather than memories told to them by someone else.

Affect Modulation and Desensitization

It is helpful to teach patients early in therapy how to rate their feelings on a scale from 1 to 10, where 1 = *no unpleasant feelings and the individual feels safe* and 10 = *the feelings are the worst they could ever be.* Ask patients what number is intolerable to them. Let them know that if they reach that level of discomfort while discussing memories, they can give you a signal you both agree on so that you can stop the discussion. It is important that you ask someone in the system to make sure everyone inside gets this message. Patients feel much safer knowing that they have some control over the depth and length of discussion of traumatic memories.

Anchors and Bridges Between Now and Then

It is often helpful to have patients hold a familiar object in their hand to ground them in the present. This helps them recognize that they are not actually back in the trauma, but in your office in the present. Although some patients with poor boundaries may ask to hold your hand, do not do this. With patients who have DID, it is important to keep physical boundaries clear and firm. Instead, let patients hold a blanket, a teddy bear, or any other object that serves as a reminder that they are safe and in the present. You may have to remind them where they are and what year it is when an alter becomes frightened and feels the abuse is still occurring. Some patients like to carry versions of a Greek worry stone. These are smooth flat rocks or pieces of marble that have an encouraging word, such as *strength*, on them.

Containment Imagery

Having patients visualize placing their memories into an area of containment, such as boxes, vaults, safes, or files that are put into a cabinet, is extremely helpful. Assure patients that the memories can stay in these containers until they choose to retrieve them. Some patients like to imagine special locks added to these containers. You can encourage them to let alters, such as a teen or internal self-helper, facilitate containment. Many of my patients choose to place the memories in "boxes" that they "hide" somewhere in my bookcases or behind or under my couch. Essentially, this technique allows patients to leave the memories in your office until they are ready to deal with them.

Sometimes an alter needs to be contained; this may be an angry part that wants to hurt the system, for example. This can be done safely but requires the cooperation of the part to be contained as well as the rest of the inside system. It is important that confinement or containment never be abusive. I have been able to have parts agree to stay in their room for a while with everything they might need. Some have agreed to having a lock on the door as long as they can call for help if they need it. It may be that we are trying to allow that part to rest. Or it may be a way of protecting the system from a suicidal or homicidal alter. This technique can work well for a while and may be written into a safety agreement. However, it cannot be relied on too frequently because it may begin to feel punitive to the alter. It is important not to create a situation in which any alter feels he or she is being punished. Quite often, alters in this situation seem to stay put for a while, but they tend to emerge at a later time when they feel ready or when things have settled down.

Safe Spaces

Help patients move from the memory to a safe space that you have identified before intense memory work. Sometimes a child alter can go inside the system and sit with an older, supportive alter. Some alters like to go inside to a beach, a quiet room, or a nice field, for example. One of my patients felt extremely safe floating in a boat with her feet dangling in the water as she looked at surrounding cliffs. Another alter liked being on a hill picking blueberries. Others enjoyed simply being at the beach. Another loved making dolls. We have used this imagery successfully after difficult sessions, as well as over the phone during crisis calls.

Distancing and the Use of Artificial Dissociation

Using the past tense and the third person offers added safety. For example, say things such as, "What was happening back then?" or "Tell me what the little girl noticed then." This technique allows them to observe and distance themselves rather than feel. It is much easier talk about what one is seeing or observing rather than what one is experiencing.

Cognitive Rather than Feeling Lines of Questioning

Try using phrases such as, "What are you thinking now?" rather than "What are you feeling?" Bypassing the feelings allows the patient to tolerate presentation of traumatic material. This simple change in words can truly make a difference in the patient's feelings of safety in treatment.

Movie Screens, Television, or DVD Techniques

Have patients put the memory on a movie screen, TV, or DVD. Instruct them to imagine they are sitting in front of a control panel.

They have control and can start, stop, rewind, freeze, or blur the frame. They can eject the DVD at any time. They can even change the channel.

Positional Change in the Memory

Help the patient gain another perspective. You might say, "Let yourself move off the bed from under the abuser and float to any place that feels safer in the room. Now you can watch what is happening. You can move behind or above the abuser." This encourages distancing so that the memory can be experienced with diminished physicality and emotion. Many patients actually feel pain or discomfort in the part of their body being affected by the abuse, such as the chest, vaginal area, or breasts. This technique can help reduce some of that discomfort.

Time Distortion

Patients are often afraid of the memories. They worry that they will have to reexperience the abuse as if it were happening all over again. For many individuals with DID, the episodes went on for a long time and occurred repeatedly. You can let patients know that although the particular experience lasted a long time, the memory and their telling about the event can be short. Tell them that they can remember all they need to know and need recall nothing more.

Recovering From the Memory

Memory work can be scary for the patient at several points. Anticipation of memory work to be done can lead to great anxiety. Sometimes alters call, e-mail, or send a text and cancel appointments to avoid doing the work. When this happens, it is important to talk with the patient to be certain he or she is ready to proceed. Sometimes the patient becomes overwhelmed during recollection of particularly difficult memories. If you have prepared well for this work, you can generally find a bigger, stronger alter or combination of alters that can be called on to pluck the victim out of the abusive situation she is currently remembering or reexperiencing and take her to a safe spot. The memories truly feel real to patients with DID, which is why grounding, explained earlier, makes it easier for them to recognize that these are memories, not something happening in the present—they are not actually back in the traumatic situation. During memory work, I have had other alters enter the scene and push the abuser under water or incapacitate the offender in some way to protect the part that is being hurt. This is often an empowering feeling for the system.

If patients get overwhelmed during this work, they can be put into a deeper trance state to rest and relax. It is often a good idea to use some relaxation techniques such as visualization or abdominal breathing as one alter goes back inside and the host emerges at the end of a session. Memory work can be unsettling, and patients report that it often takes hours to feel comfortable again. So be sure you and your patient have discussed what he or she will be doing after a session if memory work is planned. I often request that a patient check in with me later in the day after a difficult session, but it does not always happen. I think this is related to the fact that full recovery from a hypnotic or alter state has not occurred, and the patient may not even remember the request. Whenever possible, it is important to allow the system to have control. So I use this phenomena simply as information to process in the next session rather than being upset that the patient did not follow through with my request. I am, however, not so flexible when we are dealing with follow through on safety issues.

It is sometimes difficult to assess just how completely a patient has emerged from a trancelike state. Patients tell me that although it might appear to me that they have fully returned to an alert state with an adult alter present after memory work, it may actually take hours for them to fully recover. They report wandering around stores or missing time after leaving my office and before returning home. I often suggest that patients sit in my waiting room with a cup of tea until they feel completely ready to leave, even if they have assured me and appear to be fine. Rarely do they stay more than a few minutes. As noted earlier, they may be in a fugue state, or another alter may have taken control.

Kluft (2012) reported a promising instrument still being researched called the Howard Alertness Scale, developed by Hedy Howard in 2008. Howard felt that simply asking patients if they remained in hypnosis was conceptually flawed and that hypnosis itself continues to elude a consensual definition. Patients with DID slip in and out of trancelike states on a regular basis. This scale was developed to assess baseline pretrance alertness with alertness measured after an attempt has been made to awaken the patient from the trance state. Kluft (2012) found in one study that as many as 85% of a cohort found to be hypnotizable who initially affirmed that they were completely awake were actually continuing to experience residual hypnotic phenomena. This is unsettling in view of the importance of achieving a fully alert state and protecting the patient from leaving the office with his or her cognitions and coping impaired. So, although I remain firm that one should not use hypnosis for a search-and-find mission, it is virtually impossible to ignore the connection between the dissociative process and hypnosis. Clearly there is a lot of work to be done in this area. Even when the therapist does not induce a trance, the patient may have entered a trance state on his or her own. As psychotherapists, we must understand this process and use this phenomenon safely.

Use of Artwork and Journals

Alters frequently draw or write between sessions. It is helpful to encourage them to have a journal available to all of the parts. Ellen was kind enough to allow me to share, in this book, drawings that child alters had made during treatment.

The picture below was drawn by a young alter showing how she was locked in a closet and then punished for wetting her pants. She wrote, "mi cloz r wet." When she made this drawing, her family actually found her curled up in a ball in her closet, crying and with wet pants. It was a difficult time for her and her family, especially her son, who initially had no understanding of what was happening to his mother.

This next drawing is also by a young alter and shows the first time Ellen was taken out in a boat with her abuser to an island, where he raped her for the first time. Her family had been camping, and her grandfather requested that one of the children go with him on the boat. Everyone refused, and Ellen was selected to go. The rest of the family stood around and watched as he took her off to the island. This was particularly significant as her parents knew this man

was a pedophile. She recalls that later everyone told her that when she returned, she looked as if something inside of her had died.

Following is a letter written by an alter who wanted her husband to contact me so she could talk with me. She is frustrated because she knows other parts do not want her coming to psychotherapy.

Another helpful technique is the drawing of a timeline so that patients

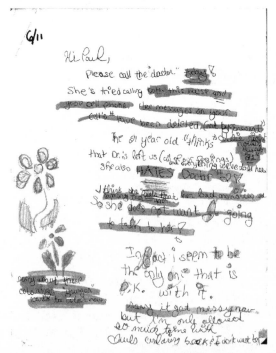

can begin to find a sense of continuity to their lives. Patients create a timeline on a poster board, filling in significant events in their lives. These may include specific events, ages, births, deaths, and the like that help patients create a sense of continuity for their lives. They begin to fill in the blank spots to develop their own sense of personal history.

Additional Comments on Treatment

I often find it helpful to have sessions twice a week. Occasionally I will see a patient three times per week, especially if we are dealing with a particular crisis or trying to avoid a hospitalization. Most patients do fine with a 50-minute hour. However, during memory work, I recommend 1.5 hour sessions to ensure the patient has settled down and an adult alter is present before the patient leaves. Some between-session calls are inevitable with these patients, but I try to keep these to a minimum. If the patient is calling too often between sessions, it probably means you are going too fast or there are not enough safeguards in place. Remember, it is up to you to establish clear boundaries and to keep them. Do not let these patients intrude on your private life. Some may try to stalk you, call constantly, or expect free sessions.

One patient who became angry at me (this is inevitable in treatment) left a nasty note on my car. We had a long discussion about boundaries and that my car was my private property, not to be intruded on. She was welcome to say whatever she wanted to me during a session or leave a note in my office, but she could not touch my car. She got the point, and it never happened again.

Be careful about setting up meetings with patients outside the office. They rarely work out and give the idea that you are their friend, not their psychotherapist. This rule is important with all patients, but patients with DID may be more likely to push for this to occur. Or you may be pulled to try to extend yourself for them.

Many years ago, one of my patients, Lilly, had become extremely isolated because of her severe drug use and DID. She had no friends and was scared to go to public places, such as a mall. Her psychiatrist and I discussed at length various ways to help this woman. With Lilly's input, we decided that she would come to my office for her session. Then we would go to a nearby mall together where we would have a

cup of coffee. We would then return to my office to process the experience. It all appeared to go well that day. However, when she arrived
for her next session a few days later, I noticed she had cut her arms
and legs badly. When I asked her what happened, she told me that
after our previous session, she had felt worse as she thought about the
fact that she didn't have anyone to go out with for a coffee. That was
my one and only attempt at conducting a session out of the office. I
would suggest you consider learning from my mistake. I would add,
however, that this same patient moved out of state a few years later.
She periodically sent me a note updating me on her condition. I was
pleased to hear recently that she is off all medications, is doing well
psychologically, has taken up hiking, and has even begun to try mountain climbing!

Transference and Countertransference

Psychotherapists treating patients with DID must be aware of issues
related to transference and countertransference. Clinicians working in
the context of DID will quickly discover that these patients are capable
of generating complex issues.

Transference

Transference responses to a psychotherapist are primarily based
on, and displaced from, significant childhood figures, especially parents and siblings. Such reactions are generally archaic, infantile, and
primary-process responses. The displacement may involve a single
traumatic event or repeated traumatic episodes. The reactions range
on a continuum from appropriate responses to reality-based stimuli to
inappropriate or psychotic responses.

With the DID patient, the psychotherapist may have to deal with
different transference issues among the alters. Transference reactions
can be precipitated by a variety of stimuli, and many are therapist-
evoked. Patients with DID are extraordinarily perceptive. They may
pick up on when the psychotherapist is not feeling well or seems a
bit distant. They may have a strong reaction when normal therapeutic
issues have to be dealt with, such as billing, vacations, or unexpected
interruptions during sessions. They may react to the color of the psychotherapist's hair or clothing. I had one patient become upset when

I wore a particular scarf one day. My initial reaction was to remove the scarf. I don't think this was particularly helpful, and we later talked about the true issues for her. It was easy to remove a scarf, but what if it were the color of my skirt or the type of sweater I had on? I certainly could not remove other articles of clothing! I immediately realized my clinical error and continued to wear scarves occasionally during her sessions. After much discussion, she was able to recall that her mother often wore scarves when disciplining her. The transference issues involved in treatment of patients with DID are generally not as well organized as in the typical patient undergoing psychoanalysis. They may be dealt with in a more piecemeal fashion, as necessary.

One area related to transference requires special mention: the act of touching a patient. If a psychotherapist touches a patient with DID, some alters might have the transference experience of the clinician being an important childhood figure who was nurturing and comforting. At the same time, other alters may experience the psychotherapist as the abuser and become terrified. This is why I am so specific about avoiding physical contact with these patients. Much later in treatment, as trauma is resolved, there are times when it may be appropriate to shake hands or even give a supportive hug. However, this is not frequent and should never be done without specific permission from all of the alters. On one occasion, I had a very young alter ask me to pinkie promise her about something important to her. It was something I felt I could promise and I joined pinkies with her for a moment. We discussed it later with the other alters, and everyone inside felt it had been important and safe for me to do this.

Putnam (1989) noted that in general, the principles enumerated by Langs (1974, p. 151) are still quite relevant for dealing with transference issues in patients with DID. These include the following:

1. Trace out the transference reaction's intrapsychic roots and determine the person or persons to whom the patient related in the past and on whom the patient's behavior toward the psychotherapist is based.

2. Identify the period from the patient's life during which the past experiences generating the transference reaction occurred. This helps to establish the level of functioning present at that

time, which may be embodied in an alter personality's reactions. The material transferred usually will contain a mixture of memories, fantasies, and past perceptions, both realistic and unrealistic.

It is important to keep in mind that transference reactions can be manifested in behaviors outside of the treatment setting. These behaviors often result in direct or indirect sabotaging of the treatment. A fairly common scenario is an alter showing up in an emergency room after having taken an overdose or having engaged in some other self-destructive behavior that may be the result of something that occurred or was discussed in a recent psychotherapy session. The alter then may relate a rather inaccurate, incomplete, or distorted version of what happened and what the psychotherapist has done. This can lead to complicating scenarios as other professionals get involved and try to "rescue" the patient without complete or accurate information.

As an example, recall Jane, the 30-year-old woman diagnosed with DID who regularly made suicidal statements. She would call me on the phone and make serious suicidal statements. I had her hospitalized on a couple of occasions. However, when she arrived at the hospital, another alter would come out and convince the staff that she was perfectly fine. I would get a call from the attending physician in the emergency room saying he had no idea why I had sent her to the hospital. Even after I explained the situation, he would note that the patient seemed fine, and he could not keep her. Clearly, he was not trained in the diagnosis and treatment of DID and appeared to have no interest in being educated.

Countertransference

Patients with DID often elicit strong countertransference reactions in therapists. Countertransference is the response on the part of the psychotherapist toward the patient that, although evoked by some event within the treatment, is primarily an outgrowth of the psychotherapist's issues in working with a particular patient. The emotions being elicited by this particular patient may also derive from important figures from the psychotherapist's own experience, such as parents and siblings. Psychotherapists living with their own teenagers may have strong unconscious reactions to the teen alters. Similarly, a hostile or sad reaction may be evoked by an alcoholic or suicidal alter if these issues are a part of the psychotherapist's past.

Countertransference reactions include feelings such as anger and hostility, sexual attraction, confusion, and the desire to distance oneself or to hold and nurture the patient. Different alters in the DID patient may actually evoke several of these feelings at once, causing further confusion. Again, I cannot emphasize enough the importance of psychotherapists being aware of these issues and getting supervision and their own therapy, especially if their countertransference issues cannot be understood and dealt with appropriately without help. The results can be deadly if you and your office are not emotionally safe for your patient. If you have your own history of trauma, please be sure that you have completely processed this in your own psychotherapy and get supervision or consultation if you think your own issues might be interfering with your patient's treatment.

Allies in Treatment

At times it is helpful to have sessions with the spouse or partner or with the children of the patient with DID. Understanding the effects of DID on the outside family system and providing support is an essential part of treatment. Referral of family members to other psychotherapists can be made as appropriate. It is generally helpful to discuss the dynamics of DID with the spouse or partner. As significant others begin to understand the DID process, they often feel validated about their own observations and report that now "things makes sense." Periodic meetings with the spouse or partner can be helpful in building and sustaining the relationship during difficult times. Healthy spouses and partners can be encouraged to work out a relationship with some of the more hostile alters, can be enlisted to support child alters, and can be reassured that with resolution of the trauma, many of the characteristics of their favorite alters will emerge and remain.

It is important to be aware of a spouse or partner who seeks to use the patient's illness for self-gratification. It is not surprising that patients with DID tend to marry people with a fair amount of their own pathology. Thus, the spouse or partner may try to elicit certain alters for certain types of sexual behavior, thereby repeating the trauma that took place. Many survivors of abuse marry abusers in an unconscious attempt to resolve their early trauma. Significant others may also try to encourage other, nonsexual but pleasant or child alters to be out. They may favor these parts and buy them presents, for example, but this type of behavior sabotages the patient's attempts at being whole and integrated. It also reinforces the idea that other parts are less desirable and may have done something wrong or bad. Alcoholism, character pathology, personality disorders, and sexual/gender identification issues also are not uncommon in spouses and partners of patients with DID.

Psychotherapists can help children of patients with DID understand their perceptions of changes in their parent. Children are often aware of minor differences or when small changes occur in a parent. They need to be helped to understand that their parent's behavior is part of an illness and not something to be imitated or manipulated for their own benefit. They should not purposely try to speak to another alter to obtain "permission" to get or do something. During crisis situations, the psychotherapist can help provide stability with reality-oriented discussions, emphasizing healthy attitudes and behavior. Children's fears about what is happening can be addressed, as can their feelings of guilt if they wish their parent would go away or die, for example.

I have met briefly with spouses and children of patients with DID fairly often. I have also worked primarily with a child of a parent with DID while a colleague saw the parent. The children repeatedly reported feeling frustrated because they would ask their parent permission to do something and get one answer. Later, when they went to do whatever it was they had requested, they got into trouble because the parent denied ever having given permission. This is confusing to both the child and parent because it was actually one alter giving permission for the activity without the knowledge or permission of the other alter or host. Additionally, as the patient gets healthier and can be more playful, their own children or spouse may wonder who is really there—their parent or the child alter. This can be frustrating for the patient, who feels a constant need to prove they are not dissociating.

Group Treatment

The literature gives no evidence that group therapy with patients with DID is effective. Meetings with family-of-origin members should only be done when it is clear they are supportive of the patient and validate his or her experiences. This is rare because the trauma that caused the DID generally occurred within the family of origin. Their participation may have been that of the active abuser or in a more passive but nonprotective role (generally a parent or parent figure). To bring an offender into the psychotherapy hour can contaminate and compromise the emotional safety of your office. If family therapy is determined to be appropriate, it should take place somewhere else and with another clinician. Occasionally this occurs when a parent truly wants to make amends. This is rare, however, and clinicians need to be alert not to be fooled into inviting offenders to sessions. I have had family-of-origin members ask the patient to get my permission to attend a session. I have always refused. I will not communicate directly with any family-of-origin member or abuser. I have no misgivings about this decision. If someone wants me to have information, he or she can always mail it to me or ask the patient to tell me. I always tell a patient if a family member has attempted to contact me.

Internal group therapy, or conversations among the alters, is often a helpful part of treatment. Individual patients are encouraged to figure out how the internal parts could communicate with each other. One patient described a large conference table where alters sat and communicated about important issues, as well as how to respond to a variety of situations. Early in treatment some of the figures were described to me as looking ghostlike. As they emerged in psychotherapy, they became more prominent at the table. Another patient said her alters communicated by cell phone. Modern technology can't be escaped! In any case, once you have identified how internal communication is handled, messages can be given to everyone, consultations about treatment can be facilitated, and treatment generally proceeds more easily.

Eye Movement Desensitization and Reprocessing

Some clinicians trained in eye movement desensitization and reprocessing (EMDR) find it a helpful technique for memory processing. Francine Shapiro (1998) developed EMDR as a way to process traumatic material more quickly than traditional psychotherapy. Patients are asked to think about a traumatic memory, and then the psychotherapist uses techniques to create bilateral stimulation of the brain. Techniques include tapping the patient's hands, waving the fingers in front of the patient's eyes, having the patient hold vibrating sensory pads, or having the patient wear a headset while listening to alternating tones. The goals are to reduce the intensity of the memory and to change negative beliefs or feelings into positive or at least neutral ones.

EMDR may be helpful as an adjunct type of treatment, but I do not believe it takes the place of processing at least some of the memories of patients with DID. In my opinion, Edna Foa (see Foa, Hembree, & Rothbaum, 2007), one of the foremost authorities on prolonged exposure therapy (in which traumatized patients repeatedly recount their trauma until it loses its disturbing power), is generally correct for patients with PTSD processing trauma. This technique works for many individuals. Patients must become desensitized to the trauma. As alters tell their part of the story, a similar type of desensitization occurs.

Bodywork

Van der Kolk's (1994) work on the neurobiology of trauma is important for clinicians considering the use of bodywork with this patient population. He has suggested that when people relive their traumatic experiences, their frontal lobes become impaired, and verbal communication becomes difficult. His ideas caught the attention of body psychotherapists who had worked with trauma patients for years. These practitioners recognized something called *somatic memory* (Wylie, 2004) and a strong mind–body connection. Proponents of bodywork, such as Reiki and massage, have found that patients will often begin to sob and experience strong physical reactions during body treatment; many feel much better after treatments.

Van der Kolk was particularly impressed with the work of Peter Levine, a therapist who began working in the filed of trauma and stress in the late 1970s. Levine received his PhD in medical biophysics from the University of California at Berkeley and also holds a doctorate in psychology from International University. He has worked in the field of stress and trauma for more than 40 years and is the developer of *Somatic Experiencing.* In his book, *In an Unspoken Voice* (2010), Levine describes his theory that trauma is locked in the body, and thus it is the body that must be accessed and healed. He notes that the psychotherapist must be able to recognize the psychoemotional and physical signs of "frozen trauma" in the patient and must learn to hear the unspoken voice of the body so that patients can safely learn to see and hear themselves. Levine believes that trauma is not a disease but a human experience, rooted in survival instincts. Thus, one can easily view DID as the survival instinct of young children unaware of complicated coping mechanisms. Dissociation and the development of parts is not taught but is innate to survival for some seriously traumatized youth. Levine is positive about patient's abilities to "unfreeze." "Trauma is a fact of life," he notes. "It does not, however, have to be a life sentence." This is a wonderful philosophy to share with patients.

Although not all clinicians were supportive of van der Kolk's endorsement of bodywork, and he certainly has caused a flurry of concern about its scientific basis, I have seen the incredibly strong connection between mind and body with DID patients. I believe that mind and body are intricately connected in all of us. Perhaps it is my background as a nurse, but I find that patients, especially those who have experienced sexual trauma, routinely experience body pain related to events they have described or tried to describe.

There are many types of bodywork, some of which I describe here. However, few have scientific data to support their use specifically in patients with DID. I have, however, had patients report positive results, in terms of relaxation and reduction of stress and muscle pain from the following techniques.

- **Swedish Massage** is a type of gentle massage used to relax muscles and increase balance and the mind's connectedness to the body, while decreasing emotional and physical stress.

- **Shiatsu** is a technique in which the therapist works on the patient's pressure points and on opening the body's energy meridians.
- **Neuromuscular therapy** is a technique that uses pressure on a patient's muscles to break the stress–tension pain cycle.
- **Acupressure** is an ancient healing art that uses the fingers to press key points on the surface of the skin to stimulate the body's natural self-curative abilities. When these points are pressed, they release muscular tension and promote the circulation of blood and the body's life force (sometimes known as *qi* or *chi*) to aid healing.
- **Integrative Manual Therapy (IMT)** is a unique set of techniques, approaches, and methodologies that address pain, dysfunction, disease, and disability. Although performed by trained physical therapists, the techniques involve touch rather than manipulation. Developed by Dr. Sharon W. Giammatteo (2002), IMT is best described as a health care process. IMT encompasses a wide range of health care practices. It achieves health and healing by taking into account the diverse systems of the human body and addressing dysfunction at the cellular level. IMT practitioners use their hands (among other tools) to diagnose and treat patients. They also have a psychotherapeutic approach that involves a process called *Integrative Diagnostics for Applied Psychosynthesis* (IDAP). IDAP is a unique process that involves gentle dialogue, visualization, and specific IMT techniques to decrease emotional stress in the body (Institute of IMT, 2011). I have had a number of trauma patients achieve relief from physical symptoms such as skeletal and muscle pain and digestive issues. I have also spoken to a couple of IMT therapists who have told me about positive work with patients with dissociative disorders.

It is not surprising that some patients with DID have a great deal of difficulty with being touched. This is particularly true during the early and middle stages of treatment. Others, however, seem to really enjoy massage, Reiki, and other types of bodywork. It is important for psychotherapists to be aware of how patients feel about these kinds of treatment. Bodywork can be helpful, but it can also bring out a great deal of emotion. As noted earlier, patients have reported suddenly sobbing during treatment and not really knowing why. Good body therapists know how to calm patients and recommend psychological treatment for patients not already involved in psychotherapy.

When possible, it is helpful to talk about and prepare patients for these possibilities before they embark on bodywork treatments. I also believe these treatments should never be done by the treating psychotherapist, even if they are trained and licensed in these areas. I had one woman, a massage therapist and social worker, tell me that she was seeing a patient for massage therapy. During her treatments, she became aware that something "seemed off" about this patient. She referred the patient to another psychotherapist, who confirmed a diagnosis of DID. The patient wanted her massage therapist to continue in both roles. The psychotherapist reported to me that she and her patient felt treatment was going well and were not having any boundary issues. Although I cannot say this was untrue and it may have worked well for them, I would not recommend this practice. There are too many opportunities for boundary violations and for difficult transference and countertransference issues to emerge. More research needs to be done in the field of bodywork to assess the benefits of these types of treatments. However, I think it would be a disservice to patients to arbitrarily exclude these types of treatment for all individuals.

Models of Treatment

Although many models of treatment have been used with DID patients, most of the literature advocates a modified form of psychodynamic psychotherapy (Braun, 1986; Greaves, 1980; Kluft, 1985, 1987). Patients with DID generally cannot tolerate the traditional unresponsive neutral response advocated by standard psychoanalysis. They will push the psychotherapist to break boundaries and can make them uncomfortable as they are pushed by the patient to be more "real" with them. Experienced psychotherapists generally find an equilibrium between the reality-based needs of the patient to be responded to in an active and direct manner and their own need to maintain a therapeutic stance toward the patient. Putnam (1989) pointed out that "one must be flexible in order to be effective with patients with DID, and yet one must be rigid with regard to certain treatment boundaries or the therapy degenerates into chaos." Such paradoxes permeate the treatment of DID.

Pais (2009) proposed a family approach to conceptualize the treatment of DID. Her use of addressing the family system both within the patient (among alters) and with the patient's spouse or children appears useful. Just as it is important to promote effective communication with all families, it is also important to improve communication with the patient's internal family. Encouraging the patient to use group talks with all family members present is helpful in both of these situations.

Many clinicians recognize that some cognitive techniques may also be helpful, especially when dealing with substance abuse issues and confronting cognitive distortions. As described earlier in the chapter, some clinicians have reported success using EMDR with trauma patients (Wiley, 2004). However, there is little research using EMDR specifically in treatment of DID.

There is also a relatively new treatment for DID called *Target Therapy* that I observed during a patient's hospitalization. Target Therapy as described on the Substance Abuse and Mental Health Services Administration (n.d.) website states that Trauma Affect Regulation: Guide for Education and Therapy (TARGET) is a

strengths-based approach to education and therapy for survivors of physical, sexual, psychological, and emotional trauma. TARGET teaches a set of seven skills (summarized by the acronym FREEDOM—Focus, Recognize triggers, Emotion self-check, Evaluate thoughts, Define goals, Options, and Make a contribution) that can be used by trauma survivors to regulate extreme emotion states, manage intrusive trauma memories, promote self-efficacy, and achieve lasting recovery from trauma. TARGET can be adapted to assist men and women from various age groups, cultures, and ethnicities who have had a variety of traumatic experiences. This program can be offered in 10–12 individual or group counseling or psychoeducational sessions conducted by clinicians, case managers, rehabilitation specialists, or teachers.

My patient Ellen was introduced to what was described to her and me as Target Therapy during a hospital stay. She was told that DID did not exist and that she needed to stay focused in the present. She was put in a group and forced to visualize things that were major triggers for her. She was so traumatized by the experience that she became catatonic. I have a difficult time understanding how denying a traumatized patient's reality, can be helpful. Perhaps Target Therapy may be more helpful with other types of trauma victims, especially veterans returning from war zones. However, the outcomes of Target Therapy remain unclear, and more research is needed, particularly on its use with patients having DID.

Hospitalization

Unfortunately, most hospitals offer little to no psychiatric treatment today. Few insurance plans cover inpatient treatment for non-emergency or suicidal/homicidal issues. Unless a patient has sufficient private funds and can go to a specialized treatment program, hospitalization is best used for safety concerns, when all other techniques have failed, or when the risk is too high to take a chance on more intensive outpatient work.

nine

Common Themes in Treatment

Treatment of patients with dissociative identity disorder (DID) is complicated and generally long term. Certainly, every patient is different. However, the following issues tend to occur regularly with patients having DID, and it is helpful to be aware of them.

Control

This is a major issue for these patients. Whenever possible, give control to the system, except in emergencies. It is important to remember that the patient is trying to maintain control both within and outside of the system. Different parts will aim to control who goes where and who does what, including in psychotherapy. One part may have every intention of being at the session and another sabotages leaving the house.

Rejection

These patients generally believe they have done something bad. As a result, they constantly expect you to reject them and will often set up situations that might lead this to happen. Acceptance and unconditional love are quite difficult for these patients to receive, even from their spouses. After all, much of the "love" they experienced as children was conditional. For example, they might have been told, "Do this sexual favor, and I will buy you an ice cream."

Secrets

Patients with DID want to keep secrets, both from you and from many of the parts inside. When the secrets are disclosed, it represents the loss of a primary object tie, a pivotal point around which their life has developed. The primary object is generally considered, in psychoanalytic terms, to be the child's necessary connection to the mother. For patients with DID, the primary object tie centers around the secrets. To let them go would eliminate this connection, which is both terrifying by nature but comforting because they can then let go of the pain. They may also feel that if no one speaks of it, it never happened. It is thus important to create an atmosphere that is safe enough for patients to talk about their abuse.

Setups and Tests

Because these patients are afraid you will turn on them as other important people in their lives have done, they will consistently test you to see if you can be trusted. If you say you will do something, you had better do it. Establish clear boundaries and keep them. If you say you will charge for missed appointments, then charge. By the same token, you have to trust them to keep their word. When you make a contract, especially regarding suicide or self-harm, be sure the contract states the patient will not hurt anyone *inside* or *outside* the body. This may sound like a simple change, but it is essential for the patient's safety. Too often, as noted previously, one alter believes he or she can hurt or kill the host or another alter without harming the others. Recommendations for incorporating no-harm contracts into the treatment process can be found in Appendix C.

What Really Happened?

When I lecture on DID, this is one of the more common questions I am asked—how do we know what really happened? You may never actually know the answer to this question. And, more important, this may not be critical, especially if there are no legal issues being pursued. Be wary of moving into the role of expert witness or forensic examiner with your DID patient. In legal situations, you may serve as a fact witness if court-ordered to do so, but whenever possible stay out of the legal system and absolutely avoid speaking of their abuse as absolute fact. You are hearing their history through the eyes of different individuals at different ages. It is important that each part feel validated about his or her personal experience. The biggest issue for the therapist is generally not legal but whether patients begin to feel relief and get better as they talk about what happened.

Anger at or Idealization of the Abuser

This is common with all victims of abuse. They may feel they need to love their abuser(s) if the abuser is a family member or friend. They may truly want to be loved by their abuser, especially if it is a parent. It is confusing and sad to feel your parent does not, or did not, love or protect you, especially when it is clear the parent either was the abuser or knew about the abuse.

Recapitulation of the Abuse

Patients will often try to consciously or unconsciously re-create the abuse both inside and outside of psychotherapy. They may try to seduce you, make you angry, or in some other fashion create a sense of danger in therapy. The clinician has to be cautious of inadvertently re-creating the abuse. For example, a patient with DID had an alter with anorexia. When she was hospitalized because she was in danger of dying, she was tied with four-point restraints and a nasogastric tube was inserted. Clearly this re-created the trauma of being held down and things being forced into her body. Because it is so common to have at least one alter with an eating disorder, clinicians must be familiar with their treatment. It is important to explore patient's feelings about food and control issues because food may have been the one thing they could control growing up. On the other hand, they may have been forced to eat or have been deprived of food.

It is important to recognize that victims of trauma can also be rather abusive at times. They push people away, avoid intimacy, and get angry with those around them. For patients with DID, these behaviors seem to be exhibited by either the host or one or two alters. Many of these behaviors can be viewed as part of what I described in my previous book, *Must I Turn the Other Cheek?* (Ducharme, 2000), as the *Cycle of Self Abuse.* In this cycle of trauma and revictimization, the victim generally has been blamed for the abuse. The offender takes no responsibility for his or her behavior. The victim may feel anger. However, anger often feels, and may in fact be, unsafe. Acting on the anger by confronting an abuser can lead to additional abuse. As children, anger was often an unacceptable emotion for them. So, even feeling the anger can lead them to blame themselves, feel shame and guilt, and develop low self-esteem and depression. In an attempt to get rid of these terrible feelings, they "forgive their offender." Because forgiveness is not really possible when they have not even processed what has happened to them, they experience a sense of failure. They ask themselves, "Why can't I forgive?" or "What is wrong with me?" They then conclude that the problem is with them. This leads to more shame, self-destructive behaviors, and an inability to treat themselves with love and dignity. As a result, they are more likely to place themselves in negative situations and can become targets for revictimization.

Sexual Acting Out and Sexual Dysfunction

Being sexual is often how these individuals were taught to please others. They may have one or more alters who are promiscuous. Obviously, this can lead to a lot of complications. One patient, a young married woman in her 30s, had an alter who enjoyed having sex with her friend's husband in their Jacuzzi. Fortunately, she was not caught, and we were able to get this alter under control and help her understand what she was doing. They may try to seduce you as well. Some patients can be persistent about this. Of course you must be clear and firm about this issue. However, it is also helpful to avoid seeing patients with this issue when you are alone in the office, such as early in the morning or late at night, because patients may be more likely to act out inappropriately when no one else is in the office. Ultimately, after a period of frustration, they will feel relieved that someone accepts them and does not want or need to abuse them.

Other patients may have difficulty having orgasms, experience pain during intercourse, or are unable to participate in certain types of sexual behavior, such as oral sex. This can be frustrating to their marital partners, especially if their sex life before marriage was good. Many individuals who were victims of incest find that after they are married, sex is once again "in the family." Marital sex can therefore be experienced in the same way as sex when they were being abused.

Guilt and Shame

These are routine issues. Earlier in the book, I mentioned my patient, Kelly, who refused to look me in the eyes for several years. When we were able to talk about it, she said she was certain that if I could see her eyes, I would be able to see the "piles of shit" that she had inside of her. When patients are able to release shameful feelings, they are free to experience happiness, make healthier choices for themselves, and surround themselves with healthier family members and friends. Sometimes letting go of one's shame means letting go of and avoiding contact with individual family members, friends, and even some religious persons to avoid being reabused. This is okay. Loving nurturing parents do not want their children surrounded by people who continue to hurt them.

Competition for the Body

Alters often fight about who should be "out." Some try to monopolize time at home, and others want to be the one out during psychotherapy. It is important to have discussions about the importance of letting everyone talk, voice their concerns, and tell their part of the history that makes up the whole person.

Desire to Meet Another Patient With DID

Meeting another person with DID may help patients feel less "crazy" or freakish, but I have rarely found it to be helpful, especially early in treatment. Some patients have told me they found it helpful to watch the television series *The United States of Tara*, a show about a woman with DID. I would not recommend this show until someone is relatively far along in their treatment. There are a number of things on the show that could be frightening and are rather inaccurate representations of treatment.

I have found that a DVD called *Lost in the Mirror, Women With Multiple Personalities*, and hosted by Diane Sawyer (Harrington, 2003), can be helpful for some patients to watch. In this video, two women diagnosed with DID, including Chris Sizemore, the woman whose story was portrayed in the film *The Three Faces of Eve*, discuss their experiences. The other woman is an articulate nurse practitioner, relatively far along in her treatment, who courageously speaks about her situation to educate the public. This same video includes commentary from three psychiatrists: Drs. David Spiegel, Herbert Spiegel, and Richard Moskovitz. I generally recommend that patients watch this with their psychotherapist and not until relatively late in the treatment process.

Drug and Alcohol Abuse

Many patients have at least one alter who has used or abused drugs or alcohol as a way of surviving the abuse and numbing their feelings. I often insist patients become involved in a drug treatment program or Alcoholics Anonymous (AA) as part of their treatment. I do not see patients who show up for their session drunk or high on drugs. I call a ride for them to be taken home. This also raises the issue of whether you can treat a patient who has a substance abuse or addiction issue. That is determined on an individual basis. On occasion, I have started treatment as a way of helping patients have enough self-esteem to feel they even deserve to get well and treat their substance abuse problem. Some patients have alters who may try to abuse benzodiazepines as a way of calming their anxiety. Therefore, it is important to be in close touch with the prescribing physician or nurse practitioner.

Patients often wonder if after integration their substance abuse issues will be gone. Generally, this is not true. As I have said previously, integration means that the separate alters are gone, but the essential components of each alter remain. Patients with an alter who abused drugs or alcohol will still have to deal with issues of addiction recovery. This can be particularly difficult because, in the past, they could either dissociate or abuse substances to get through painful times. Now they have to learn to manage stress without using either of these coping mechanisms.

Cult Abuse

This was a topic of considerable discussion in the 1980s, and many of the allegations of cult abuse remain unproven. Spanos (1996, p. 52) pointed out that there is no good evidence to support the belief in the existence of a conspiracy of murdering, child-abusing satanic cultists.

The idea that such cults exist has come to serve important political and ideological functions for some conservative Christian religious groups. Spanos was clear in his belief that "recovered memories of satanic ritual abuse are in all likelihood, therapy-induced fantasies" (p. 285).

I have worked with several patients who have described ritualistic and cultlike activities, often within a church. One patient, early in her treatment, contacted an attorney to possibly file criminal charges. The attorney refused to take the case because he felt her accounts of the abuse were too disjointed. This was not surprising because the history was being reported by different parts. When treatment was complete, the patient decided that she did not want to pursue these legal issues. She had found a sense of peace and wanted to keep it. It is important to listen carefully to the patient and remember that you (or the legal system) may never be able to know or prove what actually happened. Going through legal proceedings can be stressful and even traumatic. Most patients with DID are not able to tolerate such procedures, especially before integration has occurred. So had this woman been a victim of satanic abuse? I don't know. However, we processed these memories as if they were real. I did not challenge what she said. She improved dramatically, integrated, and continues to live a productive life.

Distribution of Energy

In the personality system, different parts have different amounts of energy. This can change at times. It is interesting that the persecutor alters can sometimes carry a lot of the energy. Although this can be scary during treatment, this energy can also be used during recovery and integration by giving and processing information. It is important to note that sometimes there are fragment personalities that carry little energy but serve a purpose for a short time. For example, they may carry parts of the "story" of a particular event or have a skill or behavior that is only needed episodically. Putnam (1989) noted that the process of energy and activity within the personality system represents one of the mechanisms through which this psychological structure evolves to meet changing needs. The psychotherapist's allegiance must be to the system, not any specific alter, and the therapist should not attempt to preserve alters who are fading away. It is also important to discuss this process as a personality system decision in which the alters, as a group, share control. At times, alters fade away for a period of time when they are not needed, only to reappear later. Rarely do alters disappear entirely on their own until the process of integration has begun and they are integrated into the whole. I have seen some alters appear to integrate on their own without a formal process after an integration of other alters has been achieved.

God and Spirituality

The issue of God and spirituality is important for most victims of abuse. I believe that if we do not explore this topic during therapy, we are being negligent. Patients are frequently angry at God or simply describe themselves as atheists. It does not specifically matter whether a patient believes in God. The issue is their perception of God if they do believe in a deity. So many of my patients have described their beliefs of God as mean, punitive, and angry. They generally do not see God as a protector. After all, He let these terrible things happen! In fact, one patient, Kelly, told me she thought of God as a "peeping Tom." The unfortunate thing is that if people believe in God but have a negative God concept, they tend to continue to punish themselves by engaging in self-harm. I have found that as treatment progressed and they felt safer and more able to protect themselves, they often softened their concepts of God or found some sort of comforting spirituality. Having a belief that there is some sense of order in the universe that does not need them to be victimized is often essential for their healing. This issue often arises for patients in programs such as AA or Narcotics Anonymous, in which God or a "Higher Power" are an important component of Recovery. Once my business partner and I were leading a group for women who had been sexually abused. We met in a room donated to us by a facility that also hosted AA meetings. The women found the 12 Steps posted on the wall so difficult to look at that we had to remove them each week until they were ready to look at their issues related to God and/or spirituality.

Forgiveness

Most patients who have been severely abused feel they must forgive their perpetrator or they are a bad person and will go to hell or have some other bad thing happen to them. I have found that when patients forgive their perpetrator prematurely, before they understand the true impact of abuse on their life, they are likely to enter into a cycle of self-abuse and sabotage their own recovery. In my book *Must I Turn the Other Cheek?* (Ducharme, 2000), I explore this concept in detail. I believe that it is unnecessary for victims of abuse to forgive their perpetrator to heal. There certainly may be times when forgiveness is healthy, appropriate, and healing. However, there are times when forgiveness is self-destructive and inappropriate.

It was said in the ancient Jewish writings known as the Mishnah that "For transgressions against God, the day of atonement atones. But for transgressions of one human being against another, the Day of Atonement does not atone until they have made peace with each other." The Talmud, another ancient Jewish text, states: "If we are guilty of sin and confess it and do not change our ways . . . so long as we cling to defilement, the uncleanliness remains." I believe that the meaning of these writings is that if you sin against God, He will forgive you. However, God will not forgive sins against another human being until the sinner has made amends. If God, in his wisdom, will not forgive someone who truly refuses to take responsibility for what the offender has done, then why should the victim, a mere mortal, worry about forgiving him or her? Forgiveness implies judgment, and it is not our job to judge others.

Richard Lord, a preacher writing a personal perspective on forgiveness, noted that in Simon Wiesenthal's (1998) book *The Sunflower,* a Jew in a Nazi concentration camp is led to the bedside of a dying German soldier. The soldier confesses that he took part in the killing of Jews and wants Wiesenthal to forgive him before he dies. Unable to do so, Wiesenthal turns and leaves the young man's side. He believes he has no right to forgive the soldier for what he did to other people. He imagines meeting the dead Jews in Heaven and hearing them ask, "What gave you the right to forgive our murderer?" Lord said he now thinks about how often in his role as preacher he has stated, "Your sins are forgiven." He now imagines a battered wife asking him who gave him the right to forgive her batterer. He now insists that there be an acceptance legally, financially, and morally of the consequences of the sin by the sinner.

I think this is a poignant statement and quite relevant to patients with DID who have suffered extensive abuse at the hands of others. It is up to the victim to forgive. However, as I discuss in the next chapter, one must truly understand what you are forgiving for it to be meaningful and not "cheap forgiveness," as one priest I was working with called it.

ten

Letting Go of the Rage

If forgiveness is not necessary for recovery, then what is? The answer is LETTING GO! Letting go of anger is essential for recovery and moving forward in life. This is not an easy task, but staying angry takes up a huge amount of emotional energy and keeps the abuser(s) in control of a person's life. Rage keeps us living in the past and unable to create and enjoy happiness in the present and future. So how does one let go?

I previously noted that patients with DID do not have to recall every episode of abuse. However, they do need to feel safe enough to be able to experience many of the feelings associated with years of trauma. As they discuss the abuse in a safe environment, much of the psychic energy connected with particular events is discharged. There becomes a desensitization, so to speak, to the traumatic material.

There are a number of ways to facilitate the process of letting go. Some of my patients have told me that as they were healing, they were able to have some form of conversation with either God or the universe and simply offer up their feelings to this Higher Power. Some have "sent" their anger skyward and into the clouds. I work with patients to help them find a way that works for them. One helpful style is imagining all of the rage as heavy stones in a backpack that they have been carting around for so many years. I will often take them through guided imagery to the edge of an ocean. There, they remove each rock one at a time from the backpack and heave it into the ocean. They can watch the rock as it hits the surface and then sinks to the bottom, never to be retrieved. A similar effect can be achieved by having the patient imagine looking down a deep well filled with calm and still water. As they drop each rock, they can watch the water as it churns with the impact and then returns to calm as the rock rests at the bottom of the well. Most patients are pretty creative and have ideas as to what will work for them, especially if you help them get started. I know that I have talked about all the reasons not to use hypnosis with patients diagnosed with DID, but guided imagery for this type of healing and letting go can be helpful. You are not introducing new concepts of abuse. You are not leading them into the unknown. These types of interventions need to be carefully planned with full consent of the patient. I generally begin with either a progressive relaxation exercise or other guided imagery for relaxation. Allowing the patient to relax and picture what she or he will be doing seems to really facilitate the process of letting go.

Mourning the Loss

We have discussed previously a variety of techniques for patients to safely process life events and emotions. As patients come to accept the truth about their abusers, who often were important members of the family with whom they were raised, they have to begin to mourn the loss of their childhood. This is a sad time. I have often referred to this experience as a "soul death." This concept rings true with many of my DID patients. Patients report going through the various stages of grief, including disbelief, bargaining with God to make it untrue, anger, sadness, and acceptance before being able to let go.

The problem is, however, that it is not just a lost childhood. It is often the loss of an entire family system. Often, the abusive family remains stuck in its negative behaviors. The victim may be blamed or at least ends up back in a family system that has no boundaries. When it is unsafe to visit relatives, even as an adult, it can be difficult. However, when it is unsafe to spend time with your parents or siblings as an adult, it can be devastating. Learning to emotionally distance themselves from these individuals may be necessary.

We all want to have a healthy family, with parents who love us and with whom we feel safe. Children need to be nurtured to develop optimally and to have a sense of safety and peace. This is often an impossibility for patients with DID. It can cause them to question their own reality and try even harder to fit in with their family of origin. This often backfires. I have seen a number a patients with DID try to reestablish family connections. Generally, if family members have not looked at their role in the abuse and taken responsibility, the patient tends to revert to old behaviors of dissociation, substance abuse, numbing of feelings, and/or self-harm. Sometimes as patients get healthier, they find a way of interacting with their family of origin. Most of the time, however, it involves remaining on "high alert" for triggers of abuse when they are together. The patient must have learned to speak up for or herself or himself, avoid uncomfortable situations, and know when to leave. It is frequently easier to mourn the loss only after the offenders are dead.

Sometimes, victims end up as caretakers of family members who either directly caused the abuse or failed to protect them from it. Kelly, the young woman I described earlier as battling alcohol and DID, ended up living with and being the primary caretaker of her elderly mother. Her mom had never really accepted that her son had been Kelly's primary offender. She adored this son and often put his needs and wants before those of her daughter. Although Kelly remained sober, she had to work hard to set boundaries and avoid compromising situations in family get-togethers. She had to speak to her brother about her mother's care and finances, and the horrific abuse that he had perpetrated remained the "pink elephant" in the room. It was never discussed. It was not until Kelly's mom passed away that she was able to truly mourn the loss of a protective family and pursue her own life.

Letting patients know that they do not have to forgive is often very freeing for them. The process of letting go of rage is hard work for both the patient and therapist, but it is truly necessary work. When they can be angry at the right person (or persons), they can begin to treat themselves with the love and respect they deserve.

eleven

Integration

Although psychotherapy may be long and arduous, patients with dissociative identity disorder (DID) can achieve integration and lead meaningful lives. Integration is the process of undoing the dissociative style
of an individual with DID and assimilating alters. Cleft, in Hammond
(1990), noted that *fusion* is the coming together of several personalities into a unity and is said to occur after several indices of the alters
have not been observed for 3 months. Many psychotherapists use the
words *integration* and *fusion* interchangeably. Integration is often more
of a process completed over several months or even years, rather than
a single event, and must always be done with full cooperation of the
entire system. In fact, it actually begins the day psychotherapy is initiated. The first time an alter reveals some information, the process of
breaking down the barriers between parts begins and continues as the
patient's history unfolds. There is a tendency for psychotherapists, and
sometimes patients, to want to rush this process. Integration should
never be attempted simply to get rid of a troublesome part. Early in my
career, I recall trying to integrate a screaming baby. It seemed as if this
infant had no real purpose in the system. The patient and I decided to
try to integrate this child. Of course it didn't work. It became clear that
someone *needed* to be crying about the horrific abuse bestowed on this
child. It was a major lesson learned.

The integration process should only be initiated when there is no
longer a need for certain parts, most often young children. Several
child alters may be blended into one child in a healing ceremony conducted during a voluntarily induced hypnotic trance. Generally, the

younger children blend into an older child. As this process continues, only the older teen and/or adult parts remain before final integration. Hammond (1990), in his book on hypnotic trances, provides several excellent examples. I have included one by Dr. Richard Kluft that I have adapted from his book in Appendix B. After a few such ceremonies have occurred with several alters, integration may spontaneously occur among other alters as treatment winds down. It is important to know that sometimes patients experience integration as a spontaneous, abrupt, or gradual process that occurs on their own. When this happens, they may complete treatment successfully without undergoing integration rituals.

When done prematurely, as noted in the case I just described, integration generally fails, and the patient and psychotherapist become frustrated when alters return. Some patients are wary of integration. They are afraid of the loss of parts of themselves. I explain to patients that when parts integrate, despite the loss of their physical being, the desired essence of their particular personality generally remains. Integration ceremonies generally describe "all that is the essence of one flowing into the other, so there is nothing really lost. But only one body and name can exist." Before an integration, they decide whose name and body will remain. We often talk about this process throughout the course of treatment. I will tell them to imagine that each alter is a river. They are separated from each other by riverbanks. I hold up my hand to show that my fingers represent the alters and the space in between the riverbanks. The riverbanks serve to keep all the parts separate and were developed to keep the parts safe. As they each share their part of the person's story, the riverbanks that separate them are no longer necessary. They do not need to keep secrets or keep the alters apart. The idea of many rivers flowing into one larger river helps patients see that even when the walls are broken down all the water remains. The formation looks different, but the contents are the same.

Despite this, some patients choose to keep an awareness of and the essence of all the parts. However, all the parts know about everyone else, and there are no secrets. Essentially, they function as a well-run corporation. There are many reasons patients choose not to integrate. Many alters associate integration with dying. Simply put, they are scared of being eliminated. Some think it is unfair that the birth child or host gets to stay. They are afraid of losing certain skills, such as artistic or athletic abilities, fluency with languages, or the ability to play or enjoy themselves.

As treatment progresses, I suggest that the host try to experience the kinds of things other parts have typically done. I encourage patients to be silly and playful with their children or spouse, without having to dissociate to a child part. As I noted previously, this can be confusing for families who have become accustomed to having a child part out during these times. Ellen told me her son would need reassurance that it was really his mom playing with him and that he need not worry that she had dissociated.

I also encourage them to spend more time in a coconscious state. This means that while another alter is out, they are watching, listening, and communicating with each other. This is especially helpful for older teens who are afraid of losing their "job" and believe the host will not function or be hurt without their help. As treatment progresses, I also suggest that each of the alters who present in a particular session stop and communicate with the host on the way in or out (or both). This technique serves to break down walls and improve communication within the system, ultimately facilitating integration.

One of the fascinating aspects of treating patients with DID is their creativity. I never fail to learn from them. I view our work as a team effort, and they play an extremely active role. Remember Casey, the first patient I diagnosed with DID? When we began discussing integration, I talked to her about two options: integration or functioning as a well-run corporation. Well, she chose Option 3. She integrated all but her teen alter, appropriately named Trouble, who she felt could keep her safe if her own strength faltered.

Most experienced psychotherapists agree that integration, although an important milestone, does not signal the end of treatment. The patient must work on developing a strong sense of integrated self. They have to adjust to dealing with difficulties without the use of dissociation. Sometimes significant others will have difficulty adjusting to the patient's new behaviors, and this may be an important time to work on marital and other family issues. It is generally easier to work with the patient's spouse and children than the family of origin. The latter may try to keep the individual in the victim role and sabotage treatment and integration. It may be necessary for the patient to keep her or his distance from certain family members during this time.

Resilience

As patients go through the process of integration, they have to learn how to socialize as a "single." Many patients with DID have spent a fair amount of time either alone or with their immediate family. Their confusing behaviors and time loss have made relationships difficult. It is important for them to learn new social skills so that they do not remain or become isolated. It is important for you to encourage them to increase their social network. It is well documented that friends help us get through tough times and increase our resilience.

Although patients with DID have certainly demonstrated an ability to survive and be resilient, they still need to learn how to cope with the everyday stressors of normal life. A combination of factors contributes to resilience or the ability to bounce back from stress. The American Psychological Association (APA; 2002) defines *resilience* as follows:

The process of adapting well in the face of adversity, trauma, tragedy, threats or even significant sources of stress—such as family and relationship problems, serious health problems, or workplace and financial stressors. It means "bouncing back" from difficult experiences."

Research has shown that resilience is ordinary, not extraordinary. People commonly demonstrate resilience. One example is the response of many Americans to the September 11, 2001, terrorist attacks and individuals' efforts to rebuild their lives. Clearly the survival skills of patients with DID demonstrate resilience. Being resilient does not mean that a person doesn't experience difficulty or distress. Emotional pain and sadness are common in people who have suffered major adversity or trauma in their lives. In fact, the road to resilience is likely to involve considerable emotional distress. Many studies show that the primary factor in resilience is having caring and supportive relationships within and outside the family. Relationships that create love and trust, provide role models, and offer encouragement and reassurance help bolster a person's resilience. Children who are badly abused for many years often lack these kinds of connections within their families. Some find one or more healthy connections outside their family of origin. Others remain isolated and need help to develop healthier relationships.

The APA has published a wonderful tip sheet available to the public on its website on resilience. APA (n.d.) makes 10 recommendations to build resilience. These recommendations are meant for everyone, not just patients with DID. However, they are particularly relevant to these patients in the third phase of treatment. The recommendations are as follows:

1. **Make connections.** Good relationships with close family members, friends, or others are important.

2. **Avoid seeing crises as insurmountable problems.** You can't change the fact that highly stressful events happen, but you can change how you interpret and respond to these events.

3. **Accept that change is a part of living.** The one constant we have in life is that nothing stays exactly the same. So, learning some flexibility is enormously helpful. Certain goals may no longer be attainable as a result of adverse situations. Accepting circumstances that cannot be changed can help you focus on circumstances that you can alter.

4. **Move toward your goals.** Do something regularly. Even small accomplishments enable you to move toward your goals.

5. **Take decisive actions.** Doing something is generally better than doing nothing.

6. **Look for opportunities for self-discovery.** People often learn something about themselves and may find that they have grown in some respect as a result of their struggle with loss.

7. **Nurture a positive view of yourself.** Developing confidence in your ability to solve problems and trusting your instincts helps build resilience.

8. **Keep things in perspective.** Avoid blowing an event out of proportion.

9. **Take care of yourself.** Pay attention to your personal needs. Engage in activities that you enjoy and find relaxing. Exercise regularly and eat well. Taking care of yourself helps to keep your mind and body primed to deal with situations that require resilience.

10. **Additional ways of strengthening resilience that may be helpful.** Some examples include writing about your deepest thoughts and feelings related to the trauma or other stressful events in your life, meditation, paying attention to spiritual practices, and maintaining a sense of hope.

Resilience is important for everyone, not just survivors of serious trauma. APA (2002) suggests we think of resilience as similar to taking a raft trip down a river. On a river, we may encounter rapids, turns, slow water, and shallows. As in life, the changes we experience affect us differently along the way. In this journey, it helps to have knowledge of the river and past experience in dealing with it. Our journey should be guided by a plan, a strategy that we consider likely to work well for us.

Perseverance and trust in our ability to work our way around boulders and other obstacles are important. We can gain courage and insight by successfully navigating our way through whitewater. Trusted companions who accompany us on the journey can be especially helpful in dealing with rapids, upstream currents, and other difficult stretches of the river. We can climb out to rest alongside the river, but to arrive at the end of our journey, we need to get back in the raft and continue.

twelve

Medication

A complete review of all medications used with patients who have dissociative identity disorder (DID) is beyond the scope of this book. However, typical types of drugs prescribed, as well as some newer and more experimental drugs, are discussed.

Medication can be an essential part of treatment for patients with DID. The key here is to be cognizant of what symptoms are being treated. All patients are different, and there is no single medication for the treatment of DID. Medications are primarily used to ameliorate nondissociative symptoms, such as depression and anxiety. Other symptoms, such as obsessive-compulsive disorder, panic, and agoraphobia, can respond well to antidepressants and anxiolytics.

One of the most common types of medications prescribed for patients with DID are selective serotonin reuptake inhibitors (SSRIs). These medications block the absorption of serotonin, a neurotransmitter in the brain, from going back into the cells that produced it. Serotonin is responsible for influencing many functions and symptoms, such as sleep, depression, and anxiety. Decreased levels of serotonin can lead to serious depression and even suicide. Typical SSRIs include Prozac, Paxil, Luvox, Celexa, and Zoloft. These medications are often effective in treating depression and anxiety.

Other classes of drugs are also used to treat mood disorders. These include the serotonin and norepinephrine reuptake inhibitors (SNRIs), such as Cymbalta, Effexor, Remeron, and trazodone. Monoamine oxides inhibitors (MAOIs) are the oldest class of antidepressants. They have severe side effects, including dangerously high blood pressure, strokes, heart attack, and even death when mixed with certain foods and drinks. Because it is difficult to be aware of and control different alters attempts to sabotage treatment, it is unlikely MAOIs would be prescribed for DID patients. The danger here is that before an accurate diagnosis is made, an unknowing physician could prescribe an MAOI to a patient with depression that is not responding to other, more frequently used antidepressants. When you have diagnosed or are treating a patient with DID, it is extremely important that you communicate with the prescribing physician about her or his medications. The patient's life may depend on it.

Unfortunately, none of these medications are free from side effects. With the SSRIs and SNRIs, significant weight gain is not uncommon. Loss of sexual desire or ability to climax is also common. Other side effects include dry mouth, blurred vision, nausea, fatigue, sleepiness, or sleep difficulties. Many of these symptoms tend to disappear after the patient has taken the medication for a while. Wellbutrin, a medication that blocks reabsorption of the neurotransmitters dopamine and norepinephrine, does not cause weight gain or sexual side effects. However, it can be rather activating and lead to increased anxiety.

It is important to remember that many patients with DID have a disordered sense of time. As a result, medication compliance can be difficult, and at times it may be necessary to have a partner, spouse, or other reliable adult administer the medications. However, because of control issues, this should only be done when absolutely necessary and with permission of the system. It is far better to find an alter who takes charge of medication management. The therapist must be aware of the potential abuse of any medication by a particular alter. As noted earlier, communication between the psychotherapist and prescribing physician is extremely important.

It is an interesting phenomenon that not all alters respond in the same way to medications. In particular, adequate surgical and dental anesthesia appears to be difficult to achieve in patients with DID (Barkin, Braun, & Kluft, 1986). As mentioned previously, anecdotal reports (Putnam, 1985) suggest that some alters may go under with anesthesia, but others can wake up on the table during the surgery, causing obvious problems for the surgical team. One of my patients reported this occurrence. If a patient is having surgery, it may be helpful to advise the surgeon and recovery room personnel that a child alter or an alter other than the original patient may be the first to wake up. I have seen a similar behavior occur in patients with the use of sleeping pills. Although the host takes her medications at night and should be "knocked out," other alters get up and engage in a variety of tasks throughout the night.

Sleep difficulties are frequent in patients with DID. At night and during darkness, they are more alone with their thoughts. Distractions are gone, and the internal parts may become more active. Nightmares and flashbacks are common. Like everyone, patients with DID function better when they are well rested, so they are likely to seek medications for sleep problem. It is imperative to remember that these medications can be used for suicide attempts and must be used with extreme caution in patients with suicidal ideation or a past history of suicide attempts.

Prazosin, a centrally active alpha-adrenergic antagonist used for treating hypertension and benign prostatic hypertrophy, has been found to substantially reduce trauma-related nightmares and other symptoms of PTSD in combat veterans. I currently have one patient with DID for whom prazosin has been helpful in significantly reducing nightmares and nighttime flashbacks. More research is needed on the effects of prazosin in the DID population.

As noted earlier, substance abuse is not uncommon in patients with DID. Opioids, prescribed for treatment of chronic pain, can lead to addiction. Suboxone (buprenorphine and naloxone) has recently been found to be helpful in treatment of opioid addiction. Buprenorphine is an opioid medication similar to morphine, codeine, and heroin. However, it produces less euphoric effects and therefore may be easier to stop taking. Naloxone, also known as Narcan, blocks the narcotic effects of opioids. This drug is administered sublingually. Although antipsychotics are not commonly used in treatment of DID, Abilify and Seroquel have been used at very low doses to treat acute symptoms of anxiety.

Again, I want to point out that medications are treating symptoms of some of the alters. Different alters have different symptoms and thus may respond differently to a variety of drugs. This makes the job of prescribing difficult, especially if there are concerns that one or more alters is suicidal. Although it may be that medications are necessary to help the patient manage symptoms sufficiently to benefit from therapy, it is effective psychotherapy in the end that resolves the major issues for patients with DID.

Conclusion

Working with patients with dissociative identity disorder (DID) is challenging but rewarding. These patients are often extremely insightful and can pick up on your moods or changes in your behaviors. I have had the privilege of working with hundreds of trauma patients and many patients with DID. I have learned so much about the strength of the human spirit and the ability to survive from each one. A word of advice when working with this patient population: Maintain a sense of humor. One patient who had a child alter that liked to play tic-tac-toe with me after difficult sessions always won. When I "complained" to her that I couldn't understand why I always lost, she promptly laughed and said, "You are looking at the board with one set of eyes. I have at least nine watching all the time!" I never did win no matter how hard I tried.

The field continues to grow, and so must we. We must understand the need to move slowly and carefully with our patients with DID. We have learned that sometimes the best treatment is maintenance of current defenses. We now understand there is no need for prolonged abreactions of traumatic material. But there is much more to learn in the effective treatment of DID.

Turkus (2013) discussed the difficulties of being a trauma psychotherapist and working with dissociative patients. She noted the challenge in sustaining an interactive, consistent relational stance, titrating the level of affect and pacing the processing of traumatic material to support the holding environment. She also pointed out the importance of clinicians understanding research and statistics. We must recognize that there are still many who deny the very existence of a disorder that to others of us has no other explanation. We must be willing to explore the use of new treatments and see what works, but we must also be cautious of using untested techniques that could potentially cause a great deal of harm. The stage has been set for further integration of neurobiology and the development of treatment and outcome studies in the trauma field.

Finally, anyone treating patients with DID must recognize the stress they are under when they listen to the horrific details that can lead to the development of DID. Trauma psychotherapists cannot go home and discuss the details of their day with their spouse and kids. A good support system and time for self-care are musts for clinicians engaging in trauma work. Engage in self-reflection. Practice mindfulness techniques. Stay in the moment and enjoy what you are doing. Take advantage of supervision and consultation with colleagues. Take time to determine your own strengths and weaknesses. Think about what you want to learn and what you need to learn. Utilize the 10 Steps to Resilience recommended by American Psychological Association (n.d.). Schedule time with friends, exercise, and take care of your own physical and mental health. And remember to laugh—it truly is great medicine! We are more authentic and believable as therapists if we live and model healthy behaviors.

It is easy to become caught up in the idea that the world is evil and children are routinely horrifically abused. Watching the news can be traumatic in itself. But, in fact, this is not true. The media just reports more of the bad. So much of the world is filled with beauty and grace. Most parents and families are loving and, if not necessarily experts at the job, want the best for their kids. With these thoughts in mind, I have found my experiences with the diagnosis and treatment of patients with DID to be challenging, at times confusing, but always rewarding. It has been a true honor to have been allowed into their lives and assist them along their journey to recovery. I wish you the same.

Appendix A

Relaxation Techniques

Abdominal Breathing

This is probably the easiest and safest of all the relaxation techniques for patients with dissociative identity disorder (DID). I ask patients to show me how they take a deep breath. Most of the time the suck in a lot of air and raise their shoulders as they do this. I explain that the breathing they are doing actually is not allowing a good breath exchange. In fact, if they continue to breathe that way, they will probably hyperventilate and begin to feel more anxious. I then explain that I will teach them a better way to breathe to help them relax.

I find it helpful if I stand up to model the breathing. After a demonstration I say:

Slowly breathe in through your nose. Hold your breath there for just a couple of seconds and now slowly exhale through your mouth. Try to make the count on your exhale twice the count on your inhale. So, if you inhale to the count of three, exhale to the count of six.

An additional helper here is to add:

What color would total relaxation be for you? What is the color of stress? OK, now when you breathe in, imagine that each breath allows you to begin to fill your body with that beautiful, relaxing color. And when you exhale, imagine that yucky color (and the stress) leaving your body. In just a few breaths, you can easily fill your body with that beautiful relaxing color and get rid of the tension and stress.

Progressive Muscle Relaxation

This is a particularly helpful form of relaxation for people who tend to dissociate because it keeps them grounded in the present. The focus remains strictly on tensing and relaxing muscles rather than trying to visualize being somewhere else. I recommend that patients practice this exercise two or three times a day after they have been taught how to do it in my office. I also provide them with a CD of the relaxation exercises they have learned.

I believe it is easier to learn when patients are lying down or in a reclining chair. However, it can also be taught in a sitting position; for many patients with DID, lying down might be frightening. This can be done with eyes open or closed. If patients feels safe enough, closed eyes allows them to focus more effectively on the actual exercise. Each muscle group is tensed for 10 seconds. I generally try to teach them abdominal breathing before we begin so that they I can insert a few nice breaths in the exercise to facilitate even deeper relaxation. I explain to patients the tighter they tense, the more the muscles relax. I sometimes show them with a rubber band how the tighter you pull the band the more it flops when released. It is important to make sure the patient has no back or neck issues that would contraindicate use of this exercise. Have them check with their physician if they have any concerns.

Script for Progressive Muscle Relaxation

We are going to begin by having you raise your arms slightly off the sofa (or chair), . . . about 6 inches. Hold your arms in that position, and when I tell you, just let them drop to your sides. That's right, just let them drop.

Now raise your arms again, but this time, squeeze your fists as tight as you can. Check the rest of your body to make sure nothing else is tensed—not your upper arms or legs, just your hands.

Now [after 10 seconds] *drop your arms and relax your hand. Notice the difference between tension and relaxation.*

Now raise your arm again, but this time tense the entire arm. Just the arm; nothing else in your body. And hold . . . relax and take a nice belly breath . . .

Now, wrinkle your nose, as if a fly had landed on it. Keep it wrinkled . . . and now relax.

Now, wrinkle your forehead, furrow your brow and hold it . . .

This time, press your tongue to the roof of your mouth and hold it . . .

Now, clench your jaw, kind of like you have a jawbreaker candy in your mouth . . . but be careful not to hurt your teeth.

This time, tense your whole face . . . tongue, forehead, nose eyes and hold it . . .

Relax and notice the difference between tension and relaxation. Relaxation feels so good...Take another belly breath and relax . . .

Now, turn your head to the left . . . feel the pull on the opposite side of your neck. Notice how good the stretch feels. And hold it . . .

Now, turn your head to the right . . . feel the stretch...

This time, roll your shoulders forward. Let your chin go forward toward your chest. Feel the nice pull across your back. It feels so good.

Now, arch your back and roll your shoulders backward. Notice that nice pull. And let it go. Feel your body becoming more relaxed as you let go of the tension.

Now, tighten your chest area. Pull the sides of your chest inward. Make sure the rest of your body is relaxed. Only your chest is tight . . .

Again, take a nice slow belly breath.

This time, imagine an elephant is trying to step on your stomach and your want to make your stomach muscles tight [or some prefer the example of trying to zip up tight jeans and pull your tummy muscles in] *. . .*

Now tighten your buttocks, squeeze hard . . . check to make your the rest of your body is relaxed.

This time, tighten your thigh muscles . . .

Now, tighten your calves. This one can be tricky so you may want to try to visualize your calves tightening. The more you practice, the easier this gets . . .

Now tighten your feet. Imagine you are wearing flip-flops and are trying to keep them on your feet. Hold it . . .

And relax.

I generally then ask patients to scan their body and see if any particular area feels tight. Often they say that their neck or shoulder area is tight, so we repeat the neck area exercises.

Once they feel they have mastered this and recognize how to tense each part of the body, I have them practice tensing their entire upper body for 10 seconds and then their lower body for 10 seconds. The goal is for this exercise to take no more than 20 seconds to complete. Some patients are able to get good results tensing the entire body for 10 seconds.

Heart-Limbic Connection

This is another relaxation technique to help calm the entire system and to aid in in falling asleep. It is meant to make a connection between the limbic system and the heart. I have had many patients find this to be helpful. It also works for the psychotherapist who is awake worrying about patients as well! Give it a try.

Place one hand over your heart. Then take three fingers on the other hand and place them on the bridge of your nose. Count slowly to somewhere between 20 and 30. Then remove your hands from those positions, and roll over. Most people fall asleep within a few minutes. It works particularly well if the progressive relaxation is completed just before this exercise.

Appendix B

Fusion/Integration Ceremony

The following fusion ceremony is my slightly adapted version of a script by Richard Kluft and appears in Dr. Corydon Hammond's (1990) book, *Handbook of Hypnotic Suggestions and Metaphors*, an amazingly helpful book with hypnotic scripts and imagery for all types of issues the patient with dissociative identity disorder may be facing. The book contains a number of fusion rituals. I generally modify the script based on the particular needs of the patient.

Remember, no fusion ritual should ever take place without extensive planning and the cooperation of the entire system. The ritual is just the final stage in a planned-out event. Before the fusion, you and the patient will have decided who is to be fused and which body and name will remain. Generally at least a few fusion ceremonies are required as different parts blend into one another. However, a formal ceremony is often not necessary for all parts. It often happens that parts seem to fuse on their own after a few formal ceremonies take place. Use whatever hypnotic induction or relaxation ritual you have found helpful with your patient. Many times I simply ask the patient to shut her or his eyes. I then ask if all the parts are ready to begin. I then say a few words about letting the entire body relax and have the patient take a few breaths. I watch the patient carefully and then ask if all the parts are ready to begin.

The Script for a Fusion Exercise

The therapist must be aware that although you may only be fusing two or three individuals at any given time, all the parts will have participated in the decision and are generally present at the ceremony.

OK . . . Today we are here to engage in the wonderful fusion of [Joan and Ann]. *You are all in a beautiful clearing on a lovely and gently sloping mountain, a place of complete privacy and safety. It is very beautiful here. You feel relaxed and comfortable. Take a minute and look around you. You will see beautiful trees and may even smell some lovely flowers. All can stand in a circle now and take one another's hands, and now move closer together. You can slide your arms gently around each other as the circle gets smaller. As you do this, you can already feel a pleasant warmth and closeness that feels good to all of you . . . even those who have no plans to join with one another today. It feels warm and very safe.*

Look above you and you will all notice a beautiful light. It rapidly becomes brighter and more radiant. It is a warming, comforting, and healing form of light that rapidly becomes beautiful, bright, and radiant—although it does not hurt your eyes at all, it is so luminous that each of you, no matter where you look, all you see is a beautiful field of light that engulfs you all. No matter where you look, there is no evidence of detail or separateness. And now the light seems to enter you as a warming current and flows back and forth, forth and back allowing you to be filled with a sense of peace and well-being.

Joan and Ann, you have chosen to become one today and are standing next to one another. As the two of you take hands, a current flows beautifully into each of you. It flows back and forth, back and forth, taking all the memories, feelings, and qualities of Joan into Ann. And all the qualities of Ann into Joan. Nothing is withheld. This feels so good as each of you blends and flows in to the other. Back and forth and forth and back. It is so complete that it seems pointless to be separate. At the count of three, the walls between Joan and Ann will gently crumble and wash away. Three: All that was Ann flows into Joan, and all that was Joan flows into Ann. It is so easy, so comfortable and safe because you have already become the same. Everything blending and joining, beautifully mixing and sharing and becoming one. And now as everything settles, you are joined now and forever at the count of two . . . Two . . . It all feels so right and so natural.

And now as the light recedes, all of you look around. Everyone feeling better, stronger, and safer . . . more complete. Where there were Joan and Ann, there is a single individual who you have all chosen to be called Joan. A single individual, stronger, more peaceful and resilient and unified now and forever at the count of one . . . One.

Now, everyone can take a nice slow breath. Joan, please nod if you are there and OK. [Nods] *Ann, nod if you remain separate* [hopefully no nod]. *Everyone else, please look around and take a moment. If you sense or know that Ann still remains separate or notices anything amiss, raise an index finger on your right hand* [hopefully nothing]. *Then, in this beautiful time and this beautiful place, let this fusion be sealed now and forever.*

Appendix C

Six Recommendations for Incorporating No-Harm Contracts Into the Treatment Process (Adapted from Hyldahl & Richardson, 2009)

It is critical to consider issues of context with regard to using no-harm contracts (NHCs), especially patients' age, developmental level, and psychosocial and medical history, as well as cultural and environmental factors, whether counseling is required or sought, and the meaning of self-injury behaviors for the patient. Interventions always need to be individualized because NHCs may be useful for some patients in certain settings but not helpful, or even harmful, in others.

It should already be clear that NHCs for patients with dissociative identity disorder (DID) are complicated. Answers to the issues just raised will vary between altars.

Hyldahl and Richardson (2009) provided the following six recommendations for using NHCs with patients who self-injure.

1. The appropriateness and usefulness of NHCs are related to the quality of the therapeutic relationship.
2. Respect autonomy and empower patients by thinking and acting collaboratively.
3. Consider reframing and renaming the NHC. Several researchers and clinicians suggest avoiding the use of the word *contract* altogether because of its perceived implications, preferring terms such as *agreement* or *promise*.

4. Place emphasis on the presence of the patient's use of healthy cognitive restructuring techniques and replacement skills rather than the absence of self-injury. Walsh (2006) noted that asking patients to give up self-injurious behaviors before they are ready might lead to feelings of failure and guilt, unproductive power struggles, and premature termination of treatment.
5. View reluctance to agree or abide by the contract as important feedback regarding the therapeutic relationship, collaborative process, the patient's current readiness to refrain from self-injury, or a combination of these.
6. Remember that contracting is just one piece of an ongoing risk assessment and treatment process.

Because of the nature of DID, it is highly likely there will be at least one alter that becomes suicidal or homicidal during treatment. Self-harm is extremely common within the system. Hospitalization, although sometimes required, can be quite traumatic. As a therapist, it is critical to attend to the very serious question of safety. As long as therapists understand that NHCs will not protect them from legal problems and that if a part expresses suicidal or homicidal ideation, the system may not be capable of agreeing to a legal contract and this is taken into consideration as part of a full lethality assessment and plan, there may be times when having a verbal or written NHC can be useful with patients diagnosed with DID.

One difference with these patients is that it is often possible to find and utilize an internal self-helper alter in these situations. Treatment of patients with DID is long term and allows some time to determine whether there is a strong enough commitment to the therapeutic relationship and internal support that would allow one to utilize a NHC. A study by Buelow and Range (2000) reported in "No-Harm Contracts: A Review of What We Know" (Lewis, 2007), notes that high school students preferred using contracts over therapy alone. I think there may be times that a teen alter feels respected and gains a certain sense of control when being given a contract. I have had young alters during the course of therapy want to make a "pinkie promise" about something important they were going to do or not do. I have also had a persecutor alter agree not to hurt another part before we had a chance to meet again. These agreements are risky, but when *used as part of a full lethality assessment,* they may be useful and help all the parts develop a sense of trust. It is important for the parts to know that there is someone inside who can take care of them and to whom they can go for help. Thus, for example, if a young part knows something bad is about to happen, that part may be able to talk with another part (often the internal self-helper), who can alert the therapist.

With this information in mind, a sample contract for use with patients with DID follows.

Sample Agreement for Suicide Prevention

Please be aware that this is not actually a legal document. If your patient commits suicide, this contract will not protect you from any legal action. You should only use this type of contract if you and the patient have established a level of trust such that you feel relatively safe using this technique. It never hurts, and I would generally recommend, that whenever possible, a support person is made aware of the situation and maintains close contact with the patient during this time. It may also be advisable to have more frequent contact, whether by phone or office visit, with the patient during this time. Although it is not secure, many patients today choose to either send a brief e-mail or text to acknowledge their ongoing safety.

Date of Agreement _____
Agreement to cover the period from _____ to
_____.

I/We agree to not knowingly or intentionally cause serious or fatal bodily harm or injury to any part, inside or out of _____ (patient's name). This includes avoiding behaviors that could result in death of the physical body of any and all parts, known and unknown, such as overdosing on medication, reckless driving, and cutting, for example.

If I or any other part, inside or out, feels unable to continue to keep this contract, I/we will immediately contact _____ (therapist) or some other identified support person or will call 911. I can also try to use the following techniques to help all of us get through this period:

1. Call an internal meeting to see if I can find internal support/ help to prevent the harm of any part.
2. I can tell myself that I have had much better days and can have them again.
3. Practice breathing/relaxation techniques.
4. Listen to music.
5. Avoid being alone and meet with a supportive family member or friend.
6. Exercise
7. Write about my feelings.
8. Draw my feelings.

This agreement remains in effect past the end date until a new agreement has been reached or I/we and all support members including _____ (therapist) agree there is no longer a need for a written agreement because I and all other parts, inside and out, feel safe and have no further desire to cause harm to myself or any other part of the system.

_____

Name of patient/date

_____

Name of therapist/date

References

Allen, J. G. (2013). Treating attachment trauma with plain old therapy. *Journal of Trauma and Dissociation, 14*, 367–374.

Allison, R. B. (1974). A new treatment approach for multiple personalities. *American Journal of Clinical Hypnosis, 17*, 15–32.

American Psychiatric Association. (2000). *Diagnostic and statistical manual of mental disorders* (4th ed., text revision). Washington, DC: Author.

American Psychiatric Association. (2013). *Diagnostic and statistical manual of mental disorders* (5th ed.). Washington, DC: American Psychiatric Association.

American Psychological Association. (n.d.). The road to resilience. Retrieved from http://helpcenter.apa.org/files/The-Road-to-Resilience.pdf

Barkin, R., Braun, B. G., & Kluft, R. P. (1986). The dilemma of drug treatment for multiple personality disorder patients. In B. G. Braun (Ed.), *The treatment of multiple personality disorder* (pp. 109–130). Washington, DC: American Psychiatric Press.

Bernstein, E. M., & Putnam, F. W. (1986). Development, reliability and validity of a dissociation scale. *Journal of Nervous and Mental Disease, 174*, 727–735.

Birnbaum, M. H., & Thompson, K. (1996). Visual function in multiple personality disorder. *Journal of American Optometric Association, 67*, 327–334.

Bliss, E. L. (1984). A symptom profile of patients with multiple personalities, including MMPI results. *Journal of Nervous and Mental Disease, 172*, 197–202.

Bliss, E. L., & Larson E. M. (1985). Sexual criminality and hypnotizability. *Journal of Nervous and Mental Disease, 173,* 522–526.

"Boris Sidis." (2005). *Dictionary of American biography base set. American Council of Learned Societies, 1928–1936.* Reproduced by the Biography Resource Center. Farmington Hills, MI: Thomson Gale.

Brand, B. L., Loewenstein, R.J., Lanius, R. Pain, C., Myrick, A. C., Classen, C. C., et al. (2012). A survey of practices and recommended treatment interventions among expert therapists treating patients with dissociative identity disorder and dissociative disorder not otherwise specified. *Psychological Trauma: Theory, Research, Practice and Policy, 4,* 490–500.

Braun, B. G. (1986). Issues in psychotherapy of multiple personality disorder. In B. G. Braun (Ed.), *The treatment of multiple personality disorder.* Washington, DC: American Psychiatric Press.

Bryant, D., Kessler, J., & Shirar, L. (1992). *The family inside: Working with the multiple.* New York: W.W. Norton.

Bruce, H. A. (1923). Boris Sidas, an appreciation. *Journal of Abnormal Psychology, 18,* 274–275.

Courtois, C. A. (2012). 21st century trauma treatment: The state of the art [online course]. *Psychotherapy Networker.* [Available at http://www.psychotherapynetworker.org]

Crabtree, A. (1986). Explanations of dissociation in the first half of the twentieth century. In J. M. Quen (Ed.), *Split minds/split brains: Historical and current perspectives.* New York: New York University Press.

deMause, L. (2002). *The emotional life of nations.* New York: Institute of Psychohistory.

Ducharme, E. (2000). *Must I turn the other cheek?* West Palm Beach, FL: Denlan Productions.

Enoch, M. D., & Trethowan W. H. (1981). *Uncommon psychiatric syndromes.* Oxford, England: Butterworth-Heinemann.

Foa, E., Hembree, E., & Rothbaum, B. (2007). *Prolonged exposure therapy.* New York: Oxford University Press.

Ford, J., & Courtois, C. (2009). *Treating complex traumatic stress disorders.* New York: Guilford Press.

Giammatteo, S. (2002). *Body wisdom.* Berkley, CA: North Atlantic Books.

Greaves, G. B. (1980). Multiple personality: 165 years after Mary Reynolds. *Journal of Nervous and Mental Disease, 168,* 577–596.

Hammond, D. C. (1990). *Handbook of hypnotic suggestions and metaphors.* New York: W.W. Norton.

Harrington, C. (Producer). (2003). *Lost in the mirror, women with multiple personalities.* Princeton, NJ: Films for the Humanities and Sciences.

Howard, H. A. (2008). The Howard Alertness Scale. *Focus, 50,* 5–6.

Hyldahl, R., & Richardson, B. (2011). Key considerations for using no-harm contracts with clients who self-harm. *Journal of Counseling and Development, 89,* 121–128.

Institute of Integrative Manual Therapy. (2011). *What is IMT?* Retrieved form http://www.instituteofimt.com/what-is-imt.php

International Society for the Study of Trauma and Dissociation. (2011). Guidelines for treating dissociative identity disorder in adults (3rd rev.). *Journal of Trauma & Dissociation, 12,* 115–187.

Ireland, W. W. (1998). Folie à deux—a mad family (Classic Text No. 35 with introduction by G. E. Berrios). *History of Psychiatry, 9,* 383–395.

Jang, K. L., Paris, J., Zweig-Frank, & Livesley, W. J. (1998). Twin study of dissociative experience. *Journal of Nervous and Mental Disease, 186,* 345–351.

Kenny, M. G. (1981). Multiple personalities and spirit possession. *Psychiatry, 44,* 337–357.

Kihlstrom, J., & McConkey, K. (1990). William James and hypnosis: A centennial reflection. *Psychological Science, 1,* 174–178.

Kluft, R. P. (1984). Treatment of multiple personality disorder: A study of 33 cases. *Psychiatric Clinics of North America, 7,* 135–148.

Kluft, R. P. (1985). The natural history of multiple personality disorder. In R. P. Kluft (Ed.), *The childhood antecedents of multiple personality.* Washington, DC: American Psychiatric Press.

Kluft, R. P. (1987). First-rank symptoms as a diagnostic clue to multiple personality disorder. *American Journal of Psychiatry, 144,* 293–298.

Kluft, R. P. (1988). The phenomenology and treatment of extremely complex multiple personality disorder. *Dissociation, 1,* 47–58.

Kluft, R. P. (2012). The same old elephant. *Journal of Trauma and Dissociation, 13,* 259–270.

Langs, R. J. (1974). *The technique of psychoanalytic psychotherapy* (Vol. 2). New York: Jason Aronson.

Levine, P. A. (2010). *In an unspoken voice: How the body releases trauma and restores goodness.* Berkeley, CA: North Atlantic Books.

Lewis, L. (2007). No-harm contracts: A review of what we know. *Suicide and Life-Threatening Behavior, 37,* 50–57.

Merskey, H. (1992). The manufacture of personalities: The production of multiple personality disorder. *British Journal of Psychiatry, 160,* 327–340.

McHugh, P. (1992, Autumn). Psychiatric misadventures. *The American Scholar,* pp. 497–510.

Nemiah, J.C. (1981). Dissociative disorders. In A. M. Freeman & H. I. Kaplan (Eds.), *Comprehensive textbook of psychiatry,* (3rd ed.). Baltimore: Williams & Wilkins.

Nijenhuis, E. R., Spinhoven, P., van der Hart, O., & Vanderlinden, J. (1996). The development and psychometric characteristics of the Somatoform Dissociation Questionnaire (SDQ–20). *Journal of Nervous and Mental Disease, 184,* 688–694.

Nijenjuis, E. R. S., Van der Hart, O., & Steele, K. (2002). Strukturale Dissoziation der Persoenlichkeit: Ueber ihre traumatischen Wurzeln und die phobischen Mechanismen, die sie in Gang halten [Structural dissociation of the personality: Traumatic origins, phobic maintenance]. In A. Hofmann, L. Reddemann, & U. Gast (Eds.), *Behandlung dissoziativer Störungen* [The treatment of dissociative disorders]. Stuttgart: Thieme Verlag.

Oesterreich, T. K. (1966). *Possession: Demonical and other among primitive races in antiquity and middle ages, and modern times.* New York: New York University Press.

Pais, S. (2009). A systemic approach to the treatment of dissociative identity disorder and false memory syndrome. *British Journal of Psychiatry, 166,* 281–283.

Pattison, E. M., & Wintrob, R. M. (1981). Possession and exorcism in contemporary America. *Journal of Operational Psychiatry, 12,* 13–20.

Piper, A., & Mersky, H. (2004). The persistence of folly: Critical examination of dissociative identity disorder. Part II. The defense and decline of multiple personality or dissociative identity disorder. *Canadian Journal of Psychiatry, 10,* 678–683.

Prince, M. (1906). *Dissociation of a personality.* New York: Longman, Green.

Putnam, F. W. (1985). Dissociation as a response to extreme trauma. In R. P. Kluft (Ed.), *The childhood antecedents of multiple personality* (pp. 64–97). Washington, DC: American Psychiatric Press.

Putnam, F.W. (1989). *Diagnosis and treatment of multiple personality disorder.* New York: Guilford Press.

Putnam, F. W. (1997). *Dissociation in children and adolescents: A developmental perspective.* New York: Guilford Press.

Putnam, F. W., Guroff, J. J., Silberman, E. K., Barban, L., & Post, R. M. (1986). The clinical phenomenology of multiple personality disorder: A review or 100 recent cases. *Journal of Clinical Psychiatry, 47,* 285–293.

Putnam, F.W., & Post, R. M. (1988). *Multiple personality disorder: An analysis and review of the syndrome.* Unpublished manuscript.

Rapaport, D. (1971). *Emotions and memory.* New York: International Universities Press.

Ross, C., Heber S., Norton, G., & Anderson, G. (1989). Dissociative Disorders Interview Schedule: A structured interview. *Dissociation, 2,* 169–189.

Sar, V., Middleton, W., & Dorahy, M. (2013). Individual and societal oppression: Global perspectives on dissociative disorders. *Journal of Trauma and Dissociation, 14,* 121–126.

Schreiber, F. R. (1973). *Sybil.* New York: Warner.

Shaffer, M., & Oakley, J. (2005). Some epistemological concerns about dissociative identity disorder and diagnostic practices. *Philosophical Psychology, 18,* 1–29.

Shapiro, F. (1998). *The breakthrough eye movement treatment for overcoming anxiety, stress and trauma.* Hoboken, NJ: Wiley.

Simon, R. I. (1999). The suicide prevention contract: Clinical, legal, and risk management issues. *Journal of the American Academy of Psychiatry and the Law, 27,* 445–450.

Spanos, N. P. (1996). *Multiple identities and false memories.* Washington, DC: American Psychological Association.

Steele, K. (1989). Looking for answers: Understanding multiple personality disorder. *Journal of Psychosocial Nursing and Mental Health Services, 27,* 4–10.

Stein, M. B., Koverola, C., Hanna, C., Torchia, M. G., & McClarty, B. (1997). Hippocampal volume in women victimized by childhood sexual abuse. *Psychological Medicine, 27,* 951–959.

Steinberg M. (1994). *The Structured Clinical Interview for DSM–IV Dissociative Disorders—Revised (SCID-D).* Washington, DC: American Psychiatric Press.

Steinberg, M. (2008). *Understanding dissociative disorders, the hidden epidemic.* Retrieved from http://www.strangerinthe mirror.com/dissociative.html

Steinberg, M., & Schnall, M. (2001). *The stranger in the mirror: Dissociation— the hidden epidemic.* Washington, DC: HarperCollins.

Stepakoff v. Kantar. 473 N.E.2d. 1131, 1133–1137 (Mass. 1985).

Stern, C. R. (1984). The etiology of multiple personalities. *Psychiatric Clinics of North America, 7,* 149–160.

Substance Abuse and Mental Health Services Administration. (n.d.). *Trauma affect regulation: Guide for education and therapy.* Retrieved from http://www.nrepp.samhsa.gov/ViewIntervention. aspx?id=258

Taylor, E. (1982). *William James on exceptional mental states: The 1986 Lowell Lectures.* New York: Scribner's.

Thigpen, C. H. & Cleckley, H. M. (1957). *The three faces of Eve.* New York: Fawcett.

Traub, C. M. (2009). Defending a diagnostic pariah: Validating the categorization of dissociative identity disorder. *South African Journal of Psychology, 39,* 347–356.t

Turkus, J. A. (2013). The shaping and integration of a trauma therapist. *Journal of Trauma and Dissociation, 14,* 1–10

van der Kolk, B. (1994). The body keeps the score: Memory and the evolving psychobiology of posttraumatic stress. *Harvard Review of Psychiatry, 1,* 253–265.

Vermetten, E., Schmahl, C., Lindner, S., Loewenstein, R. J., & Bremner, J. D. (2006). Hippocampal and amygdalar volume in dissociative identity disorder. *American Journal of Psychiatry, 4,* 630–636.

Walsh, B. W. (2006). *Treating self-injury: A practical guide.* New York: Guilford Press.

Waseem, M., Aslam, M., Switzer, R. M., & Perales, O. (2007). *Child abuse and neglect: Dissociative identity disorder.* Retrieved from http://www.emedicine.com/article/916186-overview

West, L. J. (1967). Dissociative reaction. In A. M. Freeman & H. I. Kaplan (Eds.), *Comprehensive textbook of psychiatry.* Baltimore: Williams & Wilkins.

Wiesenthal, S. (1998). *The sunflower.* New York: Knopf Doubleday.

Wylie, M. S. (2004) Beyond talk. *Psychotherapy Networker, 28,* 24–33.

Made in the USA
San Bernardino, CA
03 January 2016